MY AGING PARENT NEEDS HELP!

7 STEP GUIDE TO CAREGIVING WITH NO
REGRETS, MORE COMPASSION, AND GOING
FROM OVERWHELMED TO ORGANIZED

CYNTHIA KAYE

MIGHTY SENIORS PUBLISHING

ISBN: 978-1-959833-00-0

For my beloved parents HJK and WSK

There are only four kinds of people in the world. Those who have been caregivers. Those who are currently caregivers. Those who will be caregivers, and those who will need a caregiver.

— ROSALYNN CARTER

FREE GIFT FOR MY READERS

CONTENTS

INTRODUCTION

"I had to put my life on hold."

This is what went through Ellen's mind as she recalled taking care of her elderly mother, who suffered a major stroke. For almost a decade, Ellen focused her time, effort, and attention on meeting her mother's needs.

Her decision to provide ten years of care for her mother, who was ailing both physically and mentally, affected every job she took and had a detrimental impact on her career. She could have risen quickly to the highest ranks of her organization, but alas, she had to postpone or forego many professional advancements.

She didn't spend much on herself and used any extra money to pay for her mother's care and daily costs. Ellen made sacrifices in her personal life and sometimes overlooked her own health.

"But I have no regrets and would do it all over again," Ellen said.

Becoming her mother's caregiver was the right thing to do for her.

Deciding to take care of your ailing parent is not an easy thing to do. After all, you have your own life to live and need to consider your wants and needs too.

But knowing what you need to do and actually doing it are two different things. The plan you form in your mind may be nothing like being in the actual situation. Nothing can truly prepare you for the responsibility, stress, and emotional difficulty of caring for your aging parent.

It's easy to say –

"Yes, I can do it. How hard could it be?"

"That's my mom. Of course, I can take care of her."

But once you are thrust into it, your world is turned upside down. The challenges can seem too much for you to bear.

You frequently find yourself taking on much more than you bargained for. This situation is commonly brought on by the ever-worsening health problems that come with your parent's old age.

Constant check-ups.

The pain and suffering.

There are many ways that caregiving is hard. But it's more emotionally draining when you care for someone as near and dear as your parent.

Right before your eyes, you see your parent decline. They become increasingly needy and demanding. They can be irrational and overly sensitive, finding fault in what you do despite your best efforts at satisfying their needs.

Your aging parent may no longer recognize you. They may be too sick to talk or follow simple rules and instructions. They may have behavior problems, like shouting, hitting, or wandering away from the house.

You begin resenting your parent and the burden of their condition. You find yourself impatient with them, raising your voice, and overwhelmed in frustration. You're at home, yet it feels like you're "on call" all the time. You don't have time for yourself or anything else.

On top of it all, there's the dreadful financial worry. It seems like the medical and caregiving bills keep piling up, and you're unsure whether there will be enough resources to cover them.

Is your cup full? Are you feeling burnt out, exhausted, and overwhelmed?

Please don't beat yourself up over feeling this way. I understand where you are coming from. What you are feeling is normal. You're only human.

In all this, you must remember that caregiving is more than just caring for someone else. You have to take care of yourself, too.

There are many ways for you to overcome these feelings of frustration, worry, and fear. You can learn how to manage all of this without getting overwhelmed.

This book is a practical guide for people like you who have chosen to care for their parents in their twilight years. In addition, my hope is that this book serves as your companion as you go through your caregiving journey.

To clarify, we use the term "family caregiver" to include those who provide hands-on daily care to their aging loved ones and those who manage a paid or unpaid care team. In other words, a family caregiver may be very hands-on or hands-off. This book aims to help wherever you may be on that spectrum.

By the end of this book, the hope is that you will have a renewed sense of confidence and purpose. At this point, you may simply look at your mom or dad as a patient. The goal, however, is to have a plan, so you have the time and energy to reconnect with them again.

You can rest assured that more knowledge will lessen your worries, frustrations, and loneliness. Help is on the way.

You'll be glad to know that this book provides you with an overall game plan. I will give you tips on handling all facets of caring for an elderly parent that is realistic and action-oriented.

You'll learn to find and access available resources and advice on setting boundaries so you don't get lost amidst your caregiving duties. Finally, I will help you remember that you are much more than just a caregiver.

Your new knowledge will lead you to a more productive, balanced, and fulfilling caregiving experience. Plus, you will build a stronger relationship between patient and caregiver and, more importantly, between parent and child.

I have always had a soft spot for the elderly. One of my greatest passions is helping them and those who care for them.

This subject matter is close to home. I traversed an incredibly challenging road of caring for my elderly father in the final years of his life. After multiple strokes, he initially lost his ability to walk without a walker, then he became completely bedridden. He suffered from both severe constipation and incontinence. He also suffered from dementia and related behavioral issues.

At the same time, I was a wife, a mother to three young children, and juggling multiple part-time jobs on top of my caregiving duties.

I was also caring for (and still care for) my elderly mother, who has Stage 4 lung cancer and degenerative disc disease. I understand how difficult this can be.

This leads to why I wanted to write this book.

I do not claim to be an expert on caregiving. I am not a nurse or medical practitioner. I'm a regular person who went through the challenges of being a family caregiver.

I suffered through months and years of trying to figure out how to navigate the various resources and systems that nobody told me about.

As a child born to my parents late in their lives, I had few peers who were in similar situations. I felt very alone and overwhelmed with the need to understand everything on my own.

I wanted to write this book to share my experience and hopefully make the path for other caregivers a little easier.

While each of our journeys is unique, we also all share a lot of commonalities as family caregivers. We shouldn't have to recreate the wheel every time.

If sharing any of my experience, insights, and research can bring one other person some comfort, support, and practical help, then my effort will have been worth it.

Please take note that this book is not intended to be a comprehensive or authoritative reference guide.

It is more a compilation of my personal research and findings on what I found useful. It is intended to provide an overview of the issues to consider and the resources to research further.

In addition, I try to cover the various options that caregivers should evaluate for their particular situations. But naturally, I spend more time covering the options that I personally went through.

For example, I may share more tips on how to navigate caring for your loved one at home (versus at an assisted living or nursing home facility) because I'm more experienced with the former scenario.

This is not intended to suggest that one option is better than the others. It's more a result of my personal experience and what I'm most familiar with.

Caring for my aging parents has had its ups and downs. But I've learned many valuable lessons that I'd love to pass along to you.

Let this book help ease your burden and show you how to make the most of your caregiving season.

This book will cover what I describe as the seven steps to caregiving in a way that will leave you feeling more compassionate, more confident, and regret-free. These steps will make your caregiving journey more manageable and fulfilling.

Let's get a handle on this caregiving journey together. Don't get me wrong- it's not easy, but it doesn't have to be so hard. The most important thing is to know that you are not alone. There are many of us in this together.

Are you ready to become a care champion for your parents? It all starts with equipping yourself with the correct information.

WHAT YOU WILL LEARN

There is a fine line between saying "I will take care of you" and doing the actual caregiving. It's easy to say the words to someone you love, but when it comes down to the nitty-gritty of caregiving, we may want to shrink back from what we previously promised.

You love your parents. Among other things, that is the ultimate reason why you decide to give up other things and concentrate on them. But when the action of caring starts, there are things that you may forget.

You may forget that love for a while.

It feels like you just sat down once you've finished cleaning up after your mom, but then you hear the alarm ring because it's time for you to prepare her food. And as you feed her, she feels a bit irritated because of all the pain she cannot explain. So she lashes out, and in a surprising show of strength, she manages to knock the bowl of soup from your hands.

It's all you can do to stop yourself from lashing back. But sometimes, you can't help but show your irritation too. So, you slam your hand on the table. Your compassion for an ailing person is lost in all the anger and confusion.

These bursts of emotions can be fleeting. But there are those days that you carry the aftermath throughout the day, affecting your work. Now, you cannot remember where you put her bottle of pills, and you forget to load some laundry. Your otherwise organized self has gone into hiding. Who can blame you?

You are not perfect. Even a trained medical professional will have such days.

The upcoming chapters aim to make you someone who:

Gives care with no regrets

This book invites you to change your mindset. Allowing you to see the situation with your parent in a new light lets you behave and respond in healthier ways, which leads to fewer regrets. You will feel in control and at peace about how you are helping your parent.

Is compassionate

Yes, you may feel sorry for your aging loved one. But while you're sad, there's still something deeper lacking. That's where compassion comes in. When there's compassion, you have so much more empathy and perspective that you will naturally feel motivated to help them out of love rather than out of obligation.

Is organized

Just like with everything else, organization is vital. By having an overall plan and creating daily routines, you can feel confident about what needs to get done and how to manage your day calmly and with a clear mind.

Getting organized is the best weapon against feeling over-whelmed. Consider a student who sufficiently studies for an exam and feels ready for the test vs. a student who didn't study enough and feels a sense of dread.

Do you want to be the kind of person who feels prepared?

Wouldn't this person provide the best care for your loved one?

Each chapter has multiple sub-topics and will end with a brief summary outlining steps to help you implement what you have learned.

Chapter 1 is all about acceptance and mindset. It will invite you to let go of unhelpful perspectives and expectations about the caregiver role and encourage you to see things from a new lens-one that leads to a smoother caregiving journey rather than a resistant and reluctant one.

I'll introduce strategies to help you come to terms with your new role. If not yet in that role, the chapter also helps you identify signs that your aging parent may soon need a caregiver (which may very likely be you).

The main goal of the first chapter is to help hesitant and anxious caregivers reframe their mindsets and accept (and even welcome) their new role as a caregiver. Instead of asking:

"Why is this happening to me?"

You tell yourself –

"It is what it is, and now I have to figure out how to do my best in this situation."

After acceptance, it's time to take some action. Chapter 2 is where you will need to gather all the relevant facts and take inventory of your parent's situation: understanding details about their current medical, financial, housing situations, and other aspects of their daily life. A competent caregiver is organized and has a clear picture of what's happening and what needs to happen. You will find tips on how to get organized.

It's all about gathering the facts and getting clear on what needs to get done. We cover the typical duties of a caregiver. In addition, you will get many checklists and templates to help you get and stay organized.

This chapter will help you level-set the entire situation to manage your tasks with clarity and confidence.

Moving on to Chapter 3, I will go over the various resources available at the federal and local levels. I will also provide many online resources to explore. Using these resources is a great starting point. You will be able to do additional research to get information that may be pertinent to your family's particular location and situation.

Now that you have resources at your disposal, it's time to roll up your sleeves and figure out the finances. Chapter 4 reviews the various funding sources that can help determine how you and your aging loved one will pay for everything they need.

Since you take on the overall responsibility of caring for your parent, you serve double duty. The focus of paid caregivers is only on the "taking care" aspect. They leave costs and finances to the children or family members of the patient. In your case, you are an informal family caregiver, meaning, you are both the decision-making family member and the caregiver. Multiple decisions, financial, and caring aspects are all left to you. It is a big responsibility.

In this section, you will determine your loved one's monthly expenses and the overall budget for their needs. This will guide the long-term plan decisions. You will understand if there are budget shortfalls and options to generate more income for their caregiving needs. You will realize that even families with minimal means can manage if equipped with the appropriate knowledge.

Chapter 5 focuses on the various decisions you must make regarding living arrangements for your parent and the specifics of who will actually care for them.

Decisions on what to do with your ailing parent are not easy to make. Having as much information as possible will help you make the best choices for both you and your loved one. Your careful consideration now can prevent regrets later.

You can make more thoughtful, intelligent choices by organizing information and understanding the different options.

Regardless of the long-term care strategy you choose in the previous chapter, you must be familiar with the fundamentals of care for your elderly parent.

In Chapter 6, I'll show you how to provide for your loved one's well-rounded care, deal with resistance, ensure your parent's emotional and physical well-being, and use technology and tools to provide care more effectively.

But remember- it's not all about your aging parent. You must learn to care for yourself, too. That's what Chapter 7 is all about.

Preserving your physical, mental, and emotional well-being is critical. You will learn that self-care is one of the most crucial elements for keeping your sanity, living a balanced life, and giving the best care possible.

To avoid saying or doing things you will regret for the rest of your life, you must take care of yourself. This section is your practical self-care guide.

It does not end there. There's also a bonus section for you. Chapter 8 looks a bit more in-depth into one of the most prevalent conditions or feelings among caregivers: burnout.

Burnout is tiredness brought on by a persistent sense of being overburdened. Excessive and ongoing emotional, bodily, and mental stress is the cause. When you are emotionally spent, overburdened, and unable to keep up with life's constant demands, caregiver burnout occurs.

I will help you avoid, cope, and reverse burnout.

If you don't feel up to the task of caregiving, the following chapters will ease those worries.

If you are overwhelmed, let the information calm you. Knowledge is power.

Caring for an ailing parent is both challenging and rewarding. I want you to enjoy and truly be present during the remaining years with your loved one.

We are all caregivers in some capacity. This book encourages, supports, and recognizes everyone who selflessly embarks on this essential job.

You settle into a new routine after choosing caregiving as your new role.

The initial step is always the hardest. Acceptance is the first step toward positive change.

1

ACCEPT YOUR NEW ROLE

Caregiving might sneak up on you. You begin by stopping by your mother's place to help her wash her laundry or driving your father to the doctor. Next, you start doing their grocery shopping and medicine refills. You are doing more and more as time goes on. You eventually realize that you have stepped into this role to look after someone else.

Major medical events like a stroke, heart attack, or accident can lead to the need for caregiving. Perhaps you suddenly realize how dangerous your father's memory lapses have become. All of your efforts are now devoted to caring for your loved one while life, as you knew it, seems to come to an end. You settle into an unfamiliar routine after entering this new season of caregiving.

Settling into a new routine can be difficult. However, taking a step back and shifting your mindset is key to surviving (and even thriving) in this new role.

Having the right mindset didn't come naturally to me when I found myself suddenly my father's primary caregiver after his stroke. Although I had always done a lot to help my parents throughout my adult life, it was a completely different level of commitment when he suddenly became wheelchair-bound.

At first, I was ok with being at my parents' house more often due to the crisis nature of the stroke diagnosis and his release from the hospital.

However, when it sunk in that this huge commitment was a permanent situation, I started to feel very burdened and stressed. I wasn't sure how I was going to handle everything. My mindset felt very heavy and dark.

Acceptance is often the first step to shifting to a better mindset. However, one stumbling block many people encounter is looking at caregiving with a "let's get it over with" attitude.

You would be much better off getting out of that thinking trap. Instead, fully embracing your decision and role to care for your parent is your stepping stone to growth and change.

I eventually adopted a healthier mindset once I fully decided to accept and own my caregiver role. My feeling of "burden" shifted to "ownership" once I realized that it was my choice to step up and that I could have stepped away more if I really needed to. When I saw how much I uniquely could help my dad remember things once his dementia worsened, I wanted to be there more. I chose to be there, and that made all the difference.

But first off, for those of you who may not yet be in a caregiver role, but have some concerns that such time may soon be coming, let's discuss how to recognize the signs.

Caregiving on the Horizon? Identify the Signs

You come home for a family reunion and see your mom is not her usual cheerful self. Instead of being at the center of everything, she is quiet in the corner, looking indifferent to the festivities.

It helps to be alert regarding how your parents look and behave as they progress through their senior years. Doing so enables you to detect if that time has come for your aging parent to get some help. It may be time to get ready for a new role in your life.

Here are a few signs that indicate your elderly parent needs care or assistance:

They have lost a lot of weight.

When seniors stop eating properly, their weight may drop significantly. In addition, their inability to get to the grocery store, the lack of energy to finish their shopping list, or their lack of energy or motivation to prep, cook, and clean up can all cause seniors to lose weight. They might therefore be surviving on the barest essentials, leaving them lean, frail, and undernourished.

Their home is in a chaotic state.

This means that they no longer have the energy to clean up. As a result, messy and unclean homes are unpleasant and may pose health and hygiene risks.

They have mobility issues.

Older people frequently have joint pain and muscle weakness. Balance and vision issues are also common. The inability to move smoothly is a warning sign for a potentially catastrophic fall, a broken hip, and a transition to long-term care for your parent.

They look tired all the time.

Everyone slows down as they age, but seniors who are happy, healthy, and mentally sound typically have a fair bit of energy – even if it's just to walk out and get the paper, play cards with friends, etc. Conversely, if your parent seems tired, lethargic, or constantly complains about being exhausted, something else may be at play.

They fall often.

Senior falls increase the risk of traumatic brain injuries that may necessitate serious treatments such as surgical procedures. Falls also contribute to broken hips and other broken bones that often cascade into a series of rapid decline in elders. We should take any falls and fall risks seriously. Your parent must have living arrangements that ensure security and safety.

They exhibit behavioral changes.

Physical and emotional changes brought on by aging might trigger various behavioral changes. For example, it's natural for older people to experience moments of grief, rage, or the occasional memory lapse. Still, sometimes the changes are of a more severe nature that may necessitate deeper evaluation. Therefore, you should be aware of these signs.

They don't bother with mail.

An unusual mail pile-up may signify your loved one's inability to keep up with their tasks and responsibilities. See if this is a one-time thing or if this appears to be a recurring pattern of neglecting basic tasks.

. . .

Their cupboards and pantry are bare.

Some help will be required to ensure parents are nourished if things seem sparse or if your mom, who used to cook, is now surviving on crackers and cheese.

There are many other signs to look out for. You must observe to detect early signs and get a head start setting things up for the best long-term outcome for you and your loved one.

When you gradually notice these signs, you also slowly prepare yourself for what's to come. When you are prepared, it's easier to accept your new role.

Once you find yourself in the caregiver role, now what? Let's focus on the most essential ingredient for a successful caregiving journey: A Healthy Mindset.

∼

A Flurry of Emotions

There are situations in which adult children resist becoming their parent's caregivers. Or they become resentful of it. Is it typical to feel resentment when taking care of elderly parents?

Family dynamics have always been complex and challenging. Aging introduces new and unsettling wrinkles in our relationships with our parents, whether it has always been a close one, has grown distant over time, or has always been a difficult one. If you're responsible for caring for your parents, you might feel uncertain, uncomfortable, or even angry about your new position and what it entails for your daily activities.

So, yes, it's normal to feel resentful. It is normal to feel a range of emotions as a family caregiver. The boundaries of your available resources, particularly your emotional resources, are also put to the test by providing care.

You are not alone in this. When taking care of a parent, especially one that has many physical ailments, many caregivers may have the following emotions or thoughts:

- Anger
- Guilt
- Shame
- Worry
- Anxiety
- Isolation

You might experience any or all of these things at once. You may not even be aware that you're feeling them, or they might be really strong. They may also appear when you cope with emotions from unrelated life situations.

But all this does not make you a bad person. First, you must remember that you are more than just a caregiver. You might have a full-time or part-time job. You may be a parent, a volunteer, a spouse, or have other family obligations. You may have at last reached a much-anticipated retirement. Frustration and exhaustion are easily caused by adding caregiving to that already-full list.

According to a conservative estimate by the Family Caregiver Alliance, 20% of family caregivers experience depression, which is twice the general population's rate.

Family caregivers have plenty of reports of sadness, anxiety, anger, substance abuse, weight changes, and sleep disruptions.

Most people have difficulty letting go of the 'reluctant caregiver' mindset. That mindset looks at the situation as a negative burden.

According to research, the idea of burden may be split into subjective and objective burdens. While an objective burden is defined as occurrences or actions connected to poor caring experiences, the subjective burden primarily concerns the personal feelings that caregivers experience while executing the caregiving function.

This kind of "burden" thinking will not serve you well and will make things much harder. Instead, it would help to reframe your thinking.

～

When Duty Calls, Focus on Your Mindset

Becoming a family caregiver is one of the most significant decisions you'll make in your life.

You may have mulled it over and over again. You may feel like you've made the right choice in being your parent's primary caregiver. Or maybe you didn't decide at all and had no other options other than having to take this role.

In any case, I'm guessing there are a million questions you may have about how you are going to be able to manage this. Perhaps you don't know what first step to take.

When duty calls and you are unsure what to do, it is normal to panic. But take a deep breath. Before jumping into all the technicalities and how-to's, the fundamental step is to focus on your mindset.

Getting into a healthy mindset of empowerment and acceptance is arguably the single most important thing to becoming a great caregiver that so many overlook. So, let's turn to some ways that can help reset your mindset.

Determine What's In Your Control vs. Out of Your Control

Identify and focus on things you can control. Remember that you control how you act, how you feel, how you react to something, and how you decide to handle situations. Regardless of the external situation and stimuli, nobody can determine your mindset and your reactions other than you.

The well-known self-help author Wayne Dyer said, "If you change the way you look at things, the things you look at change." That is a powerful concept and one that I've found to be true.

It only takes a slight shift in one's perspective to completely alter that person's reality. One moment, you feel stuck and trapped. The next moment, you feel empowered and privileged to be able to help someone in need. How you choose to see things is really up to you.

By accepting responsibility for your role as a caregiver and accepting that it may end up being a long-term job, you regain some control over how you react to the circumstances. In addition, by recognizing the uncertainty of the entire caregiving journey, you become more empowered and in control. It no longer becomes a series of fire drills or crises, but rather, you anticipate and realize that each moment may present another unexpected challenge.

On the other hand, you must also recognize and be realistic about what you truly cannot control as a caregiver. For example, you have no control over whether your loved one has a chronic or progressive illness, and you have limited influence over how that illness will affect them. Despite your best efforts and all the research and remedies you find, sometimes nothing can stop the progression of their disease.

I experienced this sense of helplessness when my mom's lung cancer returned after successfully warding it off for two years with an alternative natural treatment. Despite my best efforts of making fresh carrot juice every day and feeding her a healthy plant-based diet, the cancer nodules came back bigger and were spreading. It was hard not to feel like I was failing. But, of course, I knew it was beyond my control.

Nor can we control the behaviors of others, including our aging parents. As a primary caregiver, it can be tempting to put on the decision-maker hat and start dictating how everything should go and how everyone should behave. You'll quickly discover that this approach is usually ineffective and will create more friction and resentment among family members.

Instead, we should recognize that despite their decline and dependence on others, our parents are still individuals who deserve to have their own opinions heard and respected. Increasing your compassion and understanding of their point of view will pave a smoother path- one that is cooperative rather than combative.

So, while you focus on providing your loved one with the best care, work toward letting go of matters and behaviors beyond your control. Even if we try, we can't do it all.

Once we come to terms with and accept those limits, we can move forward with a more profound sense of acceptance and peace. We can do our best with what's in our control and then let go of the rest.

. . .

Recognize Your Self-Worth

Realize your self-worth. It can be challenging since you are so preoccupied with caring for your loved one. However, you can't look after someone else unless you look after yourself. Being competent caregivers requires us to understand and accept that caring for ourselves is non-negotiable.

We'll go over the importance of caregiver self-care in Chapter 7 in much more detail, but it is worth mentioning here as it pertains to reframing your mindset.

You've heard this a hundred times before, but think about it: you must put on your oxygen mask on an airplane before you put it on for others. You can't help anyone if you run out of oxygen yourself! If you're serious about taking good care of your aging loved one, you need to be serious about planning for your self-care.

Being a martyr and neglecting yourself can quickly become the norm as you work to get things done and checked off your to-do list. However, it's unsustainable to maintain a frantic pace without taking breaks and setting boundaries.

You must prioritize your own needs and build them into your caregiving plan. By doing so from the get-go, you are telling your subconscious mind that your needs matter and that you must maintain balance under all circumstances. This profoundly empowers your mindset and shifts it from being a victim to taking responsibility for the situation.

Let go of harmful feelings of guilt and resentment

Identify and let go of the harmful emotions that may build up and fester within you. Let go of the guilt. Forgive yourself for the flaws or mistakes you may have made. Remember that you are only human. While you have the best intentions, your ability to help your loved one is constrained by your time, resources, and skills. Harboring unhealthy feelings of guilt or inadequacy can be crippling and immobilizing.

Remember your self-worth and recognize that setting boundaries to have your own time and priorities is an act of love, not selfishness. Nobody will benefit if you collapse due to unrelenting giving at the expense of your physical, mental, and emotional health. Guilt has no place in the heart and mind of an empowered and competent caregiver. You're doing your best, and there's no guilt in that.

Let go of the resentment. This can be challenging, especially if there's perhaps a complicated history between you and your loved one. Maybe you've never really understood each other, and this is the first time you need to spend so much time together. Maybe there was some form of abuse or mistreatment from your loved one when you were younger, with unresolved tensions. Navigating this is challenging when you suddenly need to be their caregiver.

Again, this is where knowledge of your self-worth can also be constructive. Frame the resentment in the present time and determine what is worth keeping and what is best to let go. Acknowledge your feelings from the past, and validate those emotions. You don't need to deny them or pretend they don't exist. Instead, recognize their presence but choose to let them go in light of the current circumstances.

It benefits you to let them go, forgive, and realize that some people (often, our parents) didn't and don't know better. It's no excuse, but we're better off silently forgiving them whether or not they realize it. Remember that "hurt people hurt" and work on forgiving those who have hurt us- as they may have been lashing out (and continue to lash out) due to their pain, deficiencies, and lack of understanding. Whatever it is, it no longer serves us to hold on to resentment.

Set realistic expectations of the length and scope of care

Understanding the scope of long-term caregiving is another way to reframe your mindset. Assume your caregiving season will be a marathon rather than a sprint. Top-performing runners keep their pace and refuel with nutrients and water along the way to complete their long-term race.

Take everything one step at a time.

Although nobody knows how long or short this caregiving season may last (and although it may feel like an eternity at times), the reality for all of us is that it will indeed come to an end one day. In other words, this is a finite period. Therefore, rather than looking at it as a burden or with reluctance, try to see it as an extraordinary opportunity to help someone very important to us- someone who needs the help desperately.

The Project-Into-the-Future Exercise

One thing I have found helpful in reframing my mindset is to project into the future after my loved one is gone. I stop and pretend for a moment that all the tedious work of caregiving has ended because my parent is now gone. I imagine how that would feel and what I would miss about the current time. Then I return to the present moment with a new-found appreciation and compassion for being in the here and now (despite it being so difficult).

Look at some of these comments from other caregivers when looking back at their caregiving time after their parent has passed:

"It was so exhausting to take care of Dad, and I didn't realize it at the time, but we had some wonderful moments between the madness. I miss him now and wish I could have one more day with him- incontinence and all." -Inge (53), Netherlands.

"I wish I would have spent a bit more time just sitting and talking with Mom during those final years. I was so busy just running around getting her errands done that I felt like I had no time to actually just take a breath and see how she was feeling." -Amy (47), Virginia.

"I'll always cherish my memories of watching all those hours of TV next to Dad while he'd be mumbling some nonsense I couldn't understand. I miss how he'd laugh out loud and how he'd ask to hold my hand during certain parts of the show." -Jessica (61), Illinois.

"I can still hear my mom's voice in my head. Her humming that I never paid much attention to now plays in my mind. I miss her very much." -Ryan (56), Texas.

These caregivers reminisce about the good times and now realize that what seemed like a never-ending and grueling period actually included some of their most cherished memories.

Those little moments that were so frustrating (when mom spilled the juice again!) were actually endearing (when she tried to help clean up with her thin, shaky hands). But unfortunately, we often only realize the precious moments when the caregiving season finally ends.

This doesn't have to be the case. If we can project into the future when our caregiving season ends and imagine for a moment that this is all over, perhaps we will have a renewed appreciation for the time we can share with our loved one who is still with us today.

Don't get me wrong. I don't deny that caregiving can be a grind on many levels. Physically, mentally, and emotionally. I also don't want to minimize the reality that most of us are often too exhausted, frustrated, and stretched too thin to stop and appreciate the moment.

I hear and feel you. I feel the same frustrations, resentment, anger, and overwhelming responsibility you may be struggling with. I experience the same guilt and helplessness that comes from feeling trapped, despite trying to do our best for them. Those feelings are real, and they are valid. But they don't have to define the entire caregiving experience and paint a dark cloud over our lives. We don't have to let that darkness prevail.

By taking a step back, breathing deeply, reframing our mindset, getting a handle on the big picture and tasks at hand, and educating ourselves, we can re-paint this picture with a brighter hue.

It does not have to be miserable.

We can see this caregiver experience with a positive mindset, one that comes from a place of ownership and empowerment. One that tells us that we can educate ourselves, learn new tasks, and be the best caregiver for our parents. The information and tools to access the right resources are in these chapters. We can do this.

Let me leave you with this poem that has been adapted from its original version about parenting and the last time parents do things for their children without realizing it's the last time until long after the fact. As declining seniors often resemble young children, this poem seemed very suitable to adapt for caregivers and their aging parents.

The Last Time Poem (author unknown)
From the moment you embrace your elderly
loved one in your arms as their caregiver,
you will never be the same.
You might long for the person you were before,
When you had freedom and time,
And nothing in particular to worry about.
You will know tiredness like you never knew it
before,
Days will run into days that are exactly the same,
Full of feedings and cleanings,
Incontinence changes and hospital beds,
Whining and fighting,
Naps or a lack of naps,
It might seem like a never-ending cycle.
But don't forget...
There is a last time for everything.
There will come a time when you will feed your
parent for the very last time.
They will fall asleep in their wheelchair during a
long walk,
And it will be the last time you ever push your
sleeping parent.
One day you will assist them to get into the car
for a doctor's trip,
And never transfer them that way again.
You will scrub their hair in the shower for one
last time,
And from that day on they will no longer be able
to shower anymore.
They will hold your hand with one hand while
holding their cane in the other, to cross the
road,

Then they will never be able to walk again, once
    they're bound to their wheelchair.
They will call you incessantly on the phone,
    asking you what you're doing,
And it will be the last call you get from them
    after they no longer remember how to use a
    phone.
One afternoon you will watch their favorite TV
    shows with them,
Then never watch TV together again because
    their vision has become too blurred.
They will insist that they don't need your help
    around the house,
Then they don't say much at all because they're
    sleeping most of the time.
You will take them to the notary to get some
    signatures on legal documents,
They will sign a document for the very last time.
The thing is, you won't even know it's the last
    time,
Until there are no more times. And even then, it
    will take you a while to realize.
So while you are living in these times,
remember there are only so many of them
and when they are gone, you will yearn for just
    one more day of them.
For one last time.

～

"Accept Your New Role" Summary Checklist

To summarize:

1. Know the signs for when your parent is close to needing care and assistance.

2. Take steps to reframe your caregiver mindset: determine what's in and out of your control, recognize your self-worth, let go of harmful guilt and resentment, set realistic expectations on the length and scope of care, and try the Project-Into-the Future Exercise and realize that this caregiving season won't last forever.

When there's full acceptance of your role and a complete understanding of what's in store for you, this healthy mindset gives you the best chance for a successful caregiving journey-one that won't be followed by regret.

You become empowered. You become a person who embraces a new perspective instead of someone who continues to oppose your reality.

The confusion brought on by these role reversals can frequently make the caring relationship more complicated. The process will go more smoothly if you can find ways to better understand and accept your new job as a caregiver with a healthy and empowered mindset.

2

GATHER THE FACTS AND GET ORGANIZED

According to a 2020 study conducted by the National Alliance for Caregiving and AARP, about one in five Americans are giving medical or supportive care to someone they love. However, caregiving demands a significant time and energy investment and can be difficult to manage long-term without a general plan. Therefore, it is critical to take inventory of where things stand and determine what you'll need to address before getting too far.

~

Understand the Scope of Your Duties

Getting organized and developing a clear understanding of what is happening and what needs to be done is one of the first steps to becoming a competent caretaker. Your main concern is for your parents' welfare as they age. Elder care considers a family member's emotional, mental, and physical wellness, and there are many moving parts to manage as their caregiver.

Below is a list of some typical duties that a family caregiver can expect to take on for their aging loved one:

- Examining the medications and prescription drug list and getting, organizing, and distributing medications according to schedule.
- Assisting with personal care and activities of daily living (ADLs), such as helping with toileting, bathing, grooming, incontinence care, dressing, feeding, and transferring from a bed to a chair or wheelchair.
- Grocery shopping, preparing food, and housekeeping.
- Choosing living arrangements and associated forms of care. The choices include in-home care, senior living, assisted living, memory care, and skilled nursing homes.
- Creating a budget and managing household costs.
- Managing health-related matters, including doctor's appointments, communicating with medical staff, and managing medical insurance and related paperwork.
- Being ready in an emergency, such as a fire or a natural disaster.
- Transporting them to doctor's appointments, shopping, and social events.
- Running errands.
- Keeping track of information about your elderly loved one. This includes medical history, medication lists, insurance information, and legal documents.
- Giving companionship.
- Taking care of necessary legal documents. This covers advance medical directives, trusts, durable financial powers of attorney, wills, and others.
- Assisting with any continuing medical treatment or therapy.

- Maintaining elderly loved ones' adherence to their care plan.
- Making a safe and more accessible house, taking steps to reduce accidents, and encouraging independent living.
- Keeping family members updated on the condition of your elderly loved one.

That's a long list of things to manage! But you will find it's a lot easier to get on top of it when we gather the facts and determine the overall caregiving and long-term care goals and plans.

~

Take Inventory and Gather Facts with a Master Checklist

Having a Master Caregiver Checklist is necessary to get and stay organized. Your daily tasks appear more doable when you list them all. In addition, it is easier to keep focused when you have a clear list of the things you need to complete and those you have already done.

Please refer to the Appendix to get a template Master Caregiver Checklist that you can adjust to your specific needs.

It's crucial to evaluate your current situation and anticipate what needs to be changed and put into place. In other words, it's time to roll your sleeves up and figure out your loved one's specific situation to inform an overall plan.

Here is a list of things you should do to gather the facts about where things stand today and what areas you need to research. The following paragraphs track nicely with the Master Caregiver Checklist.

.   .   .

Medical

- Examine your loved one's general health and needs for medical care. Contact their primary physician, talk about their most recent checkup, and assist in making future visits. Discuss their needs for medications and regular medical treatment. Verify you have access to your parent's medical record online and seek out requirements for that access if necessary.

- Complete the *Medical Information* section of the Master Caregiver Checklist, including all the medications, vitamins, and supplements that your loved one must take. It's better to type it in a document saved on your computer to avoid writing it out multiple times (as each new doctor will ask for this list). Indicate the pharmacy's phone number and address on the list for an easier time requesting refills. Verify that this list matches any online inventories.

- Verify with your loved one's medical team that all of these medications are necessary and that there aren't any contraindications between any of the items on the list. Eliminate anything that is deemed unnecessary and revise the list. Keep the list updated at all times.

- Print out the medications list and place a copy in a designated home area where all the medications are kept. Next, purchase your preferred medication dispenser holder (a 7-day pill holder for AM and PM is popular) and distribute all medications in the dispenser for the following 1-2 weeks. This way, you only need to refill the dispensers twice a month.

- Determine that the pharmacy has the correct point of contact and phone number on their records to contact for refills. Update the contact information as needed.

- Find the closest medical center or hospital for emergency care.
- List their illnesses and ongoing medical conditions. Then, continue researching these conditions to be educated on the prognosis, treatments, side effects, etc.
- Keep track of significant health treatments such as operations, creating a medical records binder. Use the binder to house all your medical records and notes collected from doctor appointments.
- Seek as much information as possible about the illness or conditions your elderly loved one is experiencing. Consult their physicians. Join Facebook groups and support groups. Study as much as possible to familiarize yourself with the issues you and your parent will likely face to prevent surprises. Then, if applicable to your parent, get in touch with the Alzheimer's Association or other similar support and education group based on your parent's particular illness.
- Talk to your local aging services or your loved one's doctors to find out where you can obtain training on how to lift someone properly, what you should do if their blood pressure is too high or too low, indicators of dehydration, etc.
- Prepare a "to go" bag for sudden trips to the hospital. Keep a copy of important documents, insurance cards, and IDs in the bag. Include a change of clothes, and if needed, any toileting items. Add a bottle of water and an individually packaged snack for long emergency room waits. You might also consider keeping emergency medications in this bag as well. A clear vinyl shoulder bag can be purchased online to help you or other caregivers identify the contents at a glance.

Home Safety

- Complete the *Home Safety Assessment* section of the Master Caregiver Checklist to survey your loved one's home setup.
- Identify and fix any areas that pose safety risks.
- Add required repairs to the *Things I Have To Do* section of the Master Caregiver Checklist.

Important Documents & Contacts

- Make sure all of the necessary legal documentation and paperwork is organized. Schedule a consultation with an elder law attorney if your loved one's situation is complex; otherwise, you may be able to use an online self-serve service like LegalZoom to get their basic estate planning documents in place.
- Review the *Important Documents and Contacts* section in the Master Caregiver Checklist to identify the various documents you should be gathering. This includes documents for their assets and liabilities, estate/end-of-life planning, and a list of their important contacts. Review the contracts and documents and consult with an elder law attorney for any specific questions that come up if you can't navigate them on your own.
- Complete the *Important Documents and Contacts* section in the Master Caregiver Checklist for contacts of people referenced in any estate planning documents (such as the trustee of your loved one's trust, if it is not you). Also, ask your loved one to confirm the selected people in these documents still reflect their current preferences. Finally, consult an elder law or estate

planning attorney to make any edits to existing estate planning documents.

- After reviewing the *Important Documents and Contacts* section in the Master Caregiver Checklist, add any missing documents to the *Things I Have To Do* section and start getting those documents created.

- Collect the email addresses and phone numbers of family members and friends who want to stay updated on your loved one's condition and set up a group email or text message to easily send group updates as needed. Include these contacts in the *Important Documents and Contacts* section in the Master Caregiver Checklist.

- Make a list of any social relationships, activities, and associations that your loved one enjoys. Record these names, addresses, phone numbers, and schedules (for example, for church services or bridge sessions) in the *Important Documents and Contacts* section in the Master Caregiver Checklist to help your loved one maintain their social and emotional health down the road.

- If/when the time comes, discuss end-of-life options with your loved one and their doctor. Some states have a Scope of Care form that is to be completed by the doctor and patient together that defines your parent's preferences. The content of this form is similar to that contained in an advance directive, discussed below.

- Gather other important legal documents. Among the most important are: birth certificates, marriage certificates, citizenship papers, pension benefits, deeds of property, deeds to cemetery plots, insurance policies, military discharge papers, divorce certificates, and death certificates of a spouse or parent. Use the *Important Documents and Contacts* section in the Master Caregiver Checklist to gather these documents.

Collecting these documents in one place will help when you apply for government and other resources asking for these documents.

Finances/Personal Expenses and Bills

- Talk to your loved one about their financial situation in general. Ask them about their preferences for handling their funds if they cannot do so themselves. Understanding an overview of their financial situation (e.g., number of bank accounts, financial obligations, and other financial concerns) is necessary to care for them competently. For tips on approaching these potentially awkward discussions, see Chapter 6.

- Discuss with your parent and banker whether or not you should be added to pertinent banking accounts.

- Review the *Finances/Personal Expenses and Bills* section of the Master Caregiver Checklist to collect a list of all their recurring expenses and how such bills are being paid (by check or online, etc.). Determine if any changes need to be made or if any recurring bills can be eliminated (for example, magazine subscriptions that no longer are read).

- Depending on how competent your loved one is (or is not), you may need to manage their online accounts to pay bills or manage their online presence. Collect all of your loved one's log-in credentials for their online accounts for their social media accounts, email accounts, bank accounts, utility bill-pay accounts, Netflix, Amazon, and any other online accounts. Use the *Online Accounts Information* sheet in the Master Caregiver Checklist to record this.

- Review Chapter 4 (Evaluate How to Pay for Care) and apply for any resource assistance for which you or your loved one qualify. These resources can potentially assist with in-home tasks, meal delivery, transportation, or respite care. Apply for outside government/community resources (such as Medicare/Medicaid and food programs) to maximize available resources to provide care for your loved one.

Activities of Daily Living (ADL) Tasks

- Complete the *ADL Assessment* in the Master Caregiver Checklist. Write a list of all the tasks your loved one needs help with (based on your observation and conversations with your loved one and their doctors). This will give you a sense of how much assistance they will need and whether you need to hire additional help or apply for other resources. This list will also help you create a job listing or complete an application for government resources if the time comes to get extra help.

- Based on the list of tasks or ADLs your loved one needs help with, determine whether you have the appropriate quantity and quality of equipment and tools to help with that ADL. For example, if your loved one needs help transferring (or moving from one place to another), do they have the appropriate canes, walkers, rollators, or wheelchairs? Write out a list of all the equipment that is either missing or needs replacement to place into the *Things I Have To Do* section of the Master Caregiver Checklist.

Meals/Errands

- Fill out the *Meals and Errands* section of the Master Caregiving Checklist and jot down the eating preferences of your loved one, the sources of their food, and who currently prepares the meals.
- This will help identify their meal prep and shopping needs as they become less independent. It will also help you spot any nutritional deficiencies or concerning eating patterns that may otherwise go unnoticed. Food is the best medicine, and improved nutrition can improve the health of your loved one naturally.
- Make a list of any routine errands specific to your loved one. This can include miscellaneous shopping runs, dry cleaning or other personal care tasks, post office runs, purchasing or returning items online, or other routine tasks.

Housing and Care Plan

- Discuss possible choices for long-term care housing plans with your loved one if they are open to it. Growing older might bring about new safety issues, particularly at home. Talk about the different senior housing options to determine whether your parent can still live independently or may be safer in other arrangements.
- Assist your aging parent in developing a caregiving plan to avoid uncertainties about what care may be required in the future.
- Visit the facilities you are considering whether your elderly loved one will eventually go to an assisted living or a skilled nursing home. Depending on the

timing of any potential move, you can consider bringing your loved one to the new facility for meals and gatherings to familiarize them with the new environment. Many facilities welcome visitors and arrange tours (in person or remotely through Zoom). If and when the transition occurs, these pre-visits will ease the process.

- Determine who can provide caregiving hours (e.g., family meetings among siblings) and how many hours of care each person can commit to each week. Record these commitments in the *Housing and Care Plan* section of the Master Caregiver Checklist. As discussed later in this chapter, you may also do a full-blown family plan. If the parent is to remain at home, any gaps after the family meeting will necessitate hiring caregivers or outsourcing care.

- Inform your friends and relatives that you are now caring for your elderly loved one, so they know your new commitments and time constraints, and do not be afraid to ask for assistance when needed.

- Let your employer know about your new duties as a family caregiver. This helps to socialize your employer to your situation and gives context for possible times that you may have to ask for time off or flexibility. You can also ask your human resources department if they have any resources or benefits for family caregivers. Become educated on all available resources and rights, such as FMLA (Family and Medical Leave Act), private backup care benefits provided by your employer, or possible flexible work arrangements.

The Master Caregiver Checklist will be something you can refer to again and again to ensure you have not missed anything and know what's coming up.

Schedule a family meeting after reviewing the checklist to ensure everyone can get on the same page. Work together to decide or delegate who can handle which part of the caregiving duties. Consider sharing some of the information you have gathered with your family members via your Google Drive or similar online storage option.

If there are no family members who can help, at least you are aware of that upfront and can determine how to handle things by yourself or with the aid of external resources, organizations, or paid helpers.

〜

Get Your Ducks in a Row (End-of-Life Planning and Other Important Documents)

Prepare an End-of-Life Plan

An End-of-Life Plan might sound morbid, taboo, and uncomfortable. Still, it is fundamental to make the inevitable passing of your loved one a much less stressful time.

Making decisions and organizing your parent's affairs before their passing is known as end-of-life planning. These decisions involve who your loved one wants to designate as their agent(s) to make crucial decisions for them regarding health, finances, property, and other matters.

Helping your elderly parents create an end-of-life plan will relieve you and other family members of a considerable burden down the road.

In addition, helping your aging parent do the pre-work of making important decisions concerning their health and money will make it much easier for everyone involved once your loved one is no longer able to make those decisions or after their death.

Use the *End of Life Checklist and Plan Template* in the Appendix to start this important process. Here are some steps to help your aging loved one complete their End-of-Life Plan:

Getting estate planning documents in place is a fundamental part of an End-of-Life Plan

While there is a multitude of estate planning documents that would benefit families, there are four essential documents that almost everyone, including your aging parent, should have prepared: (1) a trust, (2) a will, (3) a durable power of attorney for financial matters, and (4) an advanced medical directive for healthcare matters.

You can consult an elder law or estate planning attorney for the exact documents your parent may need. However, in some very straightforward cases, you can consider online self-service options, such as Legalzoom.com, to prepare these documents.

In addition, some employers provide affordable Group Legal Insurance as part of an employee's open enrollment for benefits, which could be an inexpensive way to hire an attorney to create these estate planning documents. The timeframe to create these documents can vary based on the attorney's workload and how quickly you get them the necessary information. As this process can span over several months, start the process as soon as possible so you have them in place well before you need them.

Trust. While some people may not need a Trust (although anyone who owns any real property or other significant assets should have a trust), you should consider whether your parent needs one. A trust holds assets in a trust fund for the benefit of a named beneficiary. It prevents the beneficiaries from going through a lengthy probate court process to distribute the deceased person's assets.

Will. People often think of a simple will instead of a trust as the main document that handles how they will distribute their entire estate after they die. However, many estate lawyers advise using a trust instead in order to avoid probate, as previously mentioned.

When using a trust, it's advised to also have a Pour-Over Will to go with the trust. This pour-over will is to transfer any lingering assets that weren't placed into the trust before the trustor's death. This is like a "catch-all net" that catches any assets that may not have made it into the trust in time and ensures that all assets are centrally managed and distributed under the trust.

Durable Power of Attorney for Finances. A power of attorney (PoA) in general is a written document that authorizes a person to represent or act on another's behalf for certain matters covered by that PoA. You can create different PoAs for different purposes, such as one to manage someone's medical decisions or financial matters or other matters as well.

A Durable Power of Attorney for financial matters appoints a designated person to step into the financial shoes of your loved one if they are mentally or physically unable to manage their finances. This is a critical document that you should have prepared to enable the designated representative (which may likely be you) to manage your parent's financial affairs, such as accessing their bank accounts and paying their credit cards.

Keep in mind that banks and financial institutions may have certain criteria for what they consider a valid PoA. It would be advisable to get your PoA approved by each financial institution while your aging loved one is still competent. This way, you're not stuck with an invalid PoA when you really need it (after your loved one is no longer capable of confirming their wishes to grant the PoA).

Advance Directive for Healthcare. An Advance Directive for Healthcare appoints a "medical power of attorney" as an agent to make critical medical decisions for your loved one when they can no longer make such decisions themselves. An Advance Directive also allows your loved one to make critical medical decisions in advance while still mentally capable.

These decisions may include things such as whether they want lifesaving measures like life support or artificial feeding to be performed or not or if they would prefer do-not-resuscitate orders. This makes it much clearer for the caregiver to make those decisions in line with what the loved one wanted.

Note: check with your state on this document's specific name and requirements as it can vary from Advance Healthcare Directive to Healthcare Directives to Advance Care Directives to something in between. Also, a "living will" is a type of Advance Directive that specifies your medical care preferences, such as the types of treatments you prefer not to receive.

The Advance Directive includes the "medical power of attorney" and the "living will" preferences in the same document, so you don't need multiple documents. Finally, check any specific validity requirements with your state legislature's website to ensure that the document you prepare will be legally accepted under your state's laws.

Assess your parent's insurance policies, pension benefits, and retirement investment plans

These policies and plans include life insurance, health insurance, disability coverage, pension benefits, homeowner's insurance, and long-term care insurance. Verify that all life or other insurance policy beneficiaries reflect your loved one's current wishes. For example, if Mom listed Dad as her beneficiary on all her insurance policies, but Dad is now gone, then you need to help Mom update all of her documents to list her new beneficiary.

While these documents are important to evaluate for their death-related benefits, it is important to check if the policies provide end-stage benefits while your loved one is in their later years. For example, check if their insurance covers home health checkups, physical therapy, mental health services, skilled nursing, or other short or long-term assistance. In addition, research whether any life insurance policy offers accelerated death payments to assist with long-term care costs.

Look for tax benefits and life insurance discounts.

Remodeling the home to make it accessible and hiring a temporary or part-time health aide to give respite for the main caregiver may be eligible for federal tax deductions for your family member. Consult with a tax advisor for your particular situation.

∽

Assemble a Family Plan and Manage Medical Professionals

Another aspect of taking inventory and getting a handle on the situation is to figure out what each family member can contribute to the care situation and get a clear understanding of your loved one's medical conditions and related treatment plans.

Let's discuss how to create a family plan and manage relationships with your loved one's medical team.

. . .

Create a family plan

A family plan outlines the agreement among siblings and other family members on the aspects of care. This plan serves to get everyone aligned and share in the responsibility of taking care of your loved one. Like any sport, everyone has a role to play for the team to succeed.

It is also important to designate a leader which will typically surface organically. This person should initiate, manage and run family meetings to discuss caregiving issues with everyone involved.

These meetings can be in person or over the phone and serve as regular touch-points so everyone is aligned. It also serves as an open forum for people to come up with new ideas, express concerns, or simply share what is on their minds.

Document the outcome of the meeting in a written format or agreement (email is fine), outlining who will be in charge of the various caregiving duties – and have everyone sign it (or at least acknowledge their receipt of a copy). It may not necessarily be a formal agreement, but it will assist in maintaining family harmony by outlining everyone's responsibilities.

Confirm that everyone received their copy and allow them to raise any conflicts or changes so everyone can be on the same page. Poor communication is the leading cause of family inter-personal troubles and can be prevented.

While every caregiving family plan will look different, here are a few tips on what to consider including in your family plan (see the Master Caregiving Checklist in the Appendix for a sample):

- The contact information for each member of the family and any friends or caregivers involved in the

care plan. By having such information, it's easier for
you to make contact in cases of emergency.

- A detailed weekly and daily schedule for your aging
  parent and the associated person responsible for care
  for each day/shift. With this schedule, you ensure that
  everything goes according to plan, and there's very
  little room for mistakes.
- The contact information for your parent's medical
  team (doctors, therapists, etc.). You need this for
  emergencies. Also, you can make important inquiries
  along the way.
- A list and dosage schedule for all medications and
  treatments. It's a good idea to have a reminder so there
  will be no skips or misses.
- A description of your parent's critical medical
  conditions and any allergies. You can refer to these in
  case there are changes in treatment and medications.
- Instructions in the event of any emergency. There will
  be no delays in case your parent needs to be
  hospitalized or in need of urgent treatment.
- Attach a copy of the Master Caregiver Checklist to the
  family plan, which will include the medications and
  medical and emergency contacts.

Decide with your family when and how often to meet to evaluate how the family plan is going and make any adjustments.

Manage Medical Professionals

Communicating and managing relationships with doctors and
other medical professionals treating your loved one is another
thing you should do as your parent's caregiver. If possible,
accompany your parents on their important doctor's visits. In
doing so, you become better educated about your loved one's

specific health conditions and can collaborate better with them as a team.

This collaboration ensures that you both understand the suggested medical course of action. If your parent has dementia or is cognitively disabled, you have an even more crucial role in keeping things in order.

When communicating with your parent's medical team, here are some questions:

What is the diagnosis? Many elderly patients don't fully understand their illness or diagnosis after speaking with the doctor. Ask until you feel the doctor has adequately described your parent's condition. Then, ask for the precise diagnosis and note the response so you can later do further research.

Is any other testing required? Doctors often rush to get to the next appointment, so they don't have much time to spend with each patient. Ask about the necessity for additional testing, what the doctor intends to learn from the tests, and when testing should occur if your parent undergoes testing or receives a diagnosis. Get copies of all test results for your records.

How will the medications impact my parent's appetite, energy levels, and mental acuity? Medications may affect appetite, resulting in poor nutrition and vitamin and mineral deficiencies. For example, painkillers and arthritis drugs may irritate the stomach, while antibiotics and stool softeners may impair taste.

Other medications can cause fatigue or brain fog. These are all things you should keep in mind. Feel free to question the genuine need for any drugs that have serious adverse side effects and ask if there's a more natural or less drastic alternative. Doctors tend to prescribe medications freely, and it's your right to question whether they are necessary.

Is there a need for supplements? Most specialists concur that food is the best source of human nutrition, not supplements. However, seniors may require vitamins or supplements if they don't eat a balanced diet due to health issues or a decline in appetite. Inquire about what kinds and dosages of supplements may help your parent.

What exercises help develop balance and coordination? Seniors are more likely to fall, which increases their risk of fractured hips and other ailments. Consult the doctor about exercises that will improve balance and coordination in older adults. This could include yoga, strength training, or just short walks. Exercise is critical in reducing the chance of falling for your loved one.

Is there a significant risk of a fall? How to prevent it? The risk of another fall doubles after the first fall. And more than 25% of seniors fall each year, according to the Centers for Disease Control and Prevention.

Ask the doctor what tests are available to assess your parent's balance if their medications are exacerbating their fall risk, and what exercises and safety precautions can assist.

How can I help my parent preserve their mental health? Seniors and doctors should discuss mental health. The doctor may be able to recommend strategies for maintaining mental health, like cognitive exercises and social engagement, or may recommend medications that can lessen the likelihood of developing mental or cognitive health problems.

Are there medication interactions? Seniors typically take a lot of medications. Unfortunately, because so many different doctors and specialists prescribe them, particular medicines may interact poorly with one another without anybody realizing it.

Utilize your loved one's routine checkups as an opportunity to conduct a thorough medication assessment with their doctor and get rid of any drugs that are no longer required.

What should we focus on between now and the next visit? Ask the doctor what your parent should focus on before their next appointment. This might include diet and exercise goals, keeping track of specific symptoms, or trialing a new medication. With this knowledge, you can concentrate on those areas and work on making progress by the next appointment.

Here are a few suggestions for processing and incorporating the doctor's advice:

Consider getting a second opinion. It is usually a good idea to get at least two opinions from separate qualified doctors to validate a particular diagnosis. Many illnesses can be complex and subtle to detect, and having multiple medical opinions will give you more confidence in the accuracy of the diagnosis.

Take the doctor's advice with a grain of salt. Use your common sense and judgment when evaluating what the doctor is recommending. Remember that doctors are trained in a certain way that may not always agree with your family's health and medical intervention philosophy.

For example, ask yourself and your loved one if they want to pursue invasive treatments like surgeries and harsh treatments like chemotherapy after you're educated on the likelihood of recovery, potential side effects and risks, and the efficacy of less invasive alternative treatments.

Keep an open mind and ask around. Talk to as many people or support groups on online forums about the illness or medical condition. Research potential alternative therapies and treatment options before pulling the trigger on the first option presented to you by the doctor.

Some Eastern or Ayurvedic Medicine alternatives might be a good first step in certain situations. Possibly looking at a holistic treatment option, such as drastically improving food/nutrition, exercise, sleep, and other lifestyle habits, could also make significant improvements.

Be open to potential creative solutions and see if there's a more natural path to healing your aging parent.

When my mother's lung cancer was returning after a year of chemotherapy, we were faced with the decision to move her onto another targeted pill therapy. She had suffered tremendous side effects from the chemo, and we knew the pill therapy would also cause multiple harmful side effects.

So rather than jumping to the pill, as the oncologist suggested, we asked to take a "break" from pharmaceutical treatments and had my mom try a natural CBD oil.

To the oncologist's amazement, my mom went for more than two years with minimal symptoms from the lung cancer just on the CBD oil (and a healthier, more plant-based diet). Those two extra years of feeling normal for my mom without the terrible side effects of pharmaceutical cancer treatments were amazing and priceless for our entire family.

"Gather the Facts and Get Organized" Summary Checklist

Taking a big step back and getting a bird's eye view of the entire situation by doing what was covered in this chapter will put you so far ahead of the pack when it comes to paving a solid foundation for a smooth and productive caregiving journey.

Whether gathering all relevant facts, drafting estate planning documents, or getting a family plan in place, invest the time now to get your ducks in a row to reap the vast benefits down the road.

I know this is a lot of information and there is a lot to learn and get done. But use these checklists and start gathering the information one by one. Take it one checklist at a time, and you'll realize how much you can get done in a relatively short amount of time if you have lists to guide you.

Reminders from this chapter:

1. Use the Master Caregiver Checklist and gather all the facts about your aging parent's current situation across the major areas of their life, including medical, home safety, documents, and finances.
2. Review the list of caregiver duties that you'll be tackling.
3. Get the estate planning documents prepared.
4. Help your parent prepare an end-of-life plan.
5. Create a family plan.
6. Manage medical professionals with clear communication.
7. Add open items to your running Things I Need To Do section of the Master Caregiving Checklist.
8. Cross off the items on your running Things I Need To Do list as you accomplish them.

The Master Caregiver Checklist and efficient planning will take your caregiving experience to the next level. Being organized will result in worrying less and preventing fire drills and crisis moments. Remember that being a well-organized caregiver will help you prioritize activities, get things done quickly, be prepared for emergencies, and have more free time for yourself. In addition, once things are set up and organized, you will free up a lot of your mental and emotional bandwidth to spend more quality time with your aging parent.

3

LEARN WHAT RESOURCES ARE AVAILABLE

Did you plan on becoming a caregiver for your loved one? You probably knew this time would come but never thought about what it would actually entail. This probably includes not realizing how expensive caregiving costs can be, especially when your aging parent is rapidly declining and needs many hours of assistance. That's why learning about potential resources will probably be one of the best investments you can make. Taking a little time upfront will save you hundreds of hours and thousands of dollars down the road.

Many resources for seniors and their caregivers vary from region to region. Therefore, I'll lay out the main programs and resources I'm familiar with (mainly in the US), but you can see these as a starting point and inspiration to do further research on similar programs in your area. Taking a few hours to do a general internet search for the resources listed throughout this chapter will give you a good idea of what you might want to look into further.

∾

Programs and Assistance

Taking care of an older family member requires a lot of work. However, national, state, and even local government programs might assist you.

This assistance comes in many forms. For example, the aid might help with finances, advocacy, respite, and many other aspects of caregiving.

~

Government Programs

Here are eight government programs for seniors you should know about:

1. **Medicare** (medicare.gov)

Medicare is the federal health insurance program for people 65 and older in the United States, those on Social Security Disability for two years, retired railroad workers, and those on kidney dialysis.

If your loved one is 65 or older in the United States and receiving Social Security retirement benefits, they should have received instructions on signing up for Medicare. If they haven't yet filed for Social Security benefits, they will need to apply for Medicare during the seven-month enrollment period starting three months before their 65th birthday.

Medicare Part A covers in-patient hospital visits, home health care, hospice care, a limited amount of nursing home care, and 80% of the cost of approved medical equipment. There are no premiums for Part A if you are receiving or eligible for Social Security retirement benefits (more on Social Security benefits below).

Note: although Social Security and Medicare are separate programs providing different services and benefits to seniors, they are intertwined. Social Security (through the Social Security Administration or SSA) takes care of enrolling people into Medicare Part A and Part B by working with the Centers for Medicare and Medicaid Services (CMS) to notify eligible seniors about signing up and applying.

Medicare Part B is similar to regular health insurance (doctor visits and preventive care). It has a monthly premium that is on a sliding scale depending on the individual's income level. This monthly premium is deducted from their monthly Social Security retirement payments. One can opt out of Part B if they already have insurance coverage (e.g., through an employer or spouse, etc.).

Medicare Part B covers medically necessary services to diagnose or treat your medical conditions and preventive services to prevent things like the flu or early detection of diseases. Part B also covers durable medical equipment, ambulance services, clinical research, mental health services, and limited outpatient prescription drugs.

Medically required equipment that a doctor recommends for use at home is also covered by Medicare Part B. Items like medical supplies, canes or crutches, wheelchairs, blood pressure monitors, blood sugar trackers, adult diapers, bed protection pads, external catheters, nebulizers, oxygen, and hospital beds may all be covered by Medicare. Patients often cover the remaining Part B deductible and 20% of the equipment's Medicare-approved cost.

Talk to your parent's doctor or other health providers about any particular services or equipment and ask them which of those are covered by Medicare. Then, work with your parent's medical team to get the right approvals to enable maximum coverage by Medicare Part B.

Seniors with little income and limited assets may qualify for the Medicare Savings Program, a subset of Medicaid benefits. In addition, your loved one's state of residency may assist in covering their hospital insurance and medical insurance premiums, in addition to any coinsurance, deductibles, and copayments, depending on the package they are qualified for.

Individuals can also enroll in Medicare Part C (also known as Medicare Advantage) as a private insurance alternative to Part B. They can also enroll in Medicare Part D, which is Medicare's prescription drug service.

In some circumstances, Medicare will also cover short-term stays in a skilled nursing facility. The nursing facility must be certified by Medicare to be covered. After a hospital stay, your parent's doctor can recommend that you undergo specialized nursing care and rehabilitation. However, care at a skilled nursing facility is only covered if your parent had a qualifying hospital stay, which means that they were officially admitted as an inpatient to a hospital for at least three straight days. This is distinct from monitoring status, which doesn't count even if they spend the night in the hospital.

Medicare Hospice Benefits.

Hospice care focuses on managing the pain and symptoms of terminally ill patients and attending to their emotional and spiritual needs at the end of life. This is the final stage of care, where the focus is on prioritizing the patient's comfort and quality of life by reducing pain and suffering rather than treatments to try to cure the illness.

Hospice care is usually provided in the patient's home and not at a hospital or treatment facility (other than short in-patient hospice stays for emergencies or a few days of respite care for the caregiver, depending on the hospice program). Hospice nurses (and bathing or other specialty assistants through hospice) do not replace the role of daily in-home caregivers, as they only come to the house a few times a week for an hour or so each visit.

In addition, once you elect hospice care for your aging parent, you effectively switch from their regular Medicare hospital coverage to at-home hospice care. This means Medicare no longer covers the costs of going to the hospital for treatments like they did in the past. So, if they were to have a heart attack while on hospice, you'd call your hospice doctor for advice on what to do, rather than calling 911.

You can stop hospice care anytime and switch back to regular hospital coverage, so there's no fear that you're locked in one way or another. However, by choosing hospice care, you're deciding that there are no more "treatments" to try to cure the illness and that you accept that your loved one has only months left and focus on making those last months as comfortable and pain-free for them.

Hospice agencies work with Medicare to provide these end-of-life hospice services, and all related costs are covered as a benefit of Medicare. A life expectancy of fewer than six months is required to qualify for hospice coverage. However, if patients survive longer than six months, they are still eligible for hospice benefits if their hospice doctor reaffirms their diagnosis as terminal. Such re-certification is required initially after 90 and 180 days and then every 60 days.

Medicare Hospice Benefits cover: hospice nurses and doctors, medication required to maintain comfort and reduce or eliminate symptoms, may require speech, occupational or physical therapy to remain comfortable or learn how to manage the changes their body is going through, and anything else that the hospice staff deems essential and connected to maintaining their comfort and managing the symptoms of their terminal illness. Medicare also covers social services, such as counseling for social or emotional issues associated with their illness or accident.

My father was on hospice for the last 12 months of his life, and the support (including emotional support) we got from our hospice nurses, staff, and caregivers was priceless. When we felt quite fearful and confused, the hospice nurses reassured us with their weekly visits to our home. We didn't feel so alone. The hospice nurse also warned me about two days before my dad's actual passing that I should get prepared. Had she not told me that, I would not have had any idea that we had such little time left with my dad.

Because of our hospice nurse, we were all able to gather and spend several quality days surrounding my sleeping dad with love before he took his final breath. I can never thank our hospice nurse enough for that gift.

Ultimately, what is or is not covered by Medicare depends on three main things:

1. Federal and state laws.
2. National coverage decisions made by Medicare on what is or is not covered.
3. Local coverage decisions made by companies on a state-by-state basis that process Medicare claims.

Staying up to date on what Medicare covers for your aging parent in your state will help you maximize the assistance your loved one can get from such coverage.

One last note: be aware that people with disabilities may be eligible for Medicare before turning 65 if they are on Social Security Disability Insurance (SSDI). We will share more on SSDI below.

2. Medicaid (medicaid.gov)

Medicaid is a federal-state partnership program that offers low-income Americans health insurance. Medicaid benefits vary from state to state. Adults who are disabled or 65 or older may be eligible for Medicaid.

Medicaid, as opposed to Medicare, provides coverage for a range of long-term care and community and home-based care services. However, applicants must fulfill strict financial standards to qualify for Medicaid coverage. According to federal regulations, each state manages its own Medicaid program. Thus, the specific qualifying requirements change. Visit Medicaid.gov to learn more about the program in general. Visit the website of your state's government to learn more about the Medicaid program there.

Keep in mind that Medicaid has different names in different states (for example, Medi-Cal in California, MassHealth in Massachusetts, TennCare in Tennessee, and MaineCare in Maine).

There are two main types of Medicaid. One is for people who reside in nursing homes, and the other is for people who live at home. The eligibility requirements are different for each and vary by state. Long-term care Medicaid can be provided both in nursing homes (referred to as "long-term care Medicaid") and in the "home and community," including in-home care, adult day care, and assisted living homes (referred to as "Home and Community Based Services" or "HCBS").

Note: Medicaid's eligibility requirements are incredibly compli-cated and time-consuming to navigate, and the application process can feel like an exercise in human perseverance and futility. In other words, getting your parent to qualify for the program can be difficult.

If you find that your parent's current monthly income is too high, don't give up. Look into programs like the Spousal Impov-erishment Rule scenarios in your state to see if your parents may qualify for Medicaid despite having higher incomes. Any income that exceeds the minimum income requirements would become the Share of Cost your parent would be responsible for (which acts like a deductible that must first be paid each month before Medicaid funds kick in). Research further for your particular state rules.

Medicaid offers services, such as long-term care in a nursing home or in the community, that are not covered by Medicare or private health insurance. For example, assistance with everyday tasks like washing, dressing, and eating are among the services offered by long-term care facilities. Through a Medicaid waiver program (such as the Home and Community-Based Services Waiver or HCBS Waiver), these services can also be accessible in your home or an assisted living facility in some states. Research what Medicaid waiver programs may be available in your state.

Medicaid also offers In-Home Supportive Services (IHSS) in California that helps patients with house cleaning, meal prep, grocery shopping, personal care, laundry, assistance at medical visits, and protective monitoring for people with mental disabilities. Depending on an assessment of your loved one's care needs, IHSS will pay for a certain number of care-giving hours per month. This extra financial support can be a huge help. You can learn more by researching IHSS's eligibility requirements or similar programs in your loved one's state.

3. **Social Security Administration (SSA) Benefits** (ssa.gov)

There are four main types of SSA benefits:

(i) Retirement Benefits.

For the worker:

Your elderly parent can apply for Social Security retirement as early as 62 or as late as 70 (they can still apply any time after 70 and should do so as soon as possible because there's no benefit increase by waiting past 70). Benefits from Social Security offer qualifying retired adults and those with disabilities, as well as their spouses, children, and survivors, a portion of a replacement income. A person's retirement benefit amount is determined by their past wages, the year of their birth, and the age at which they first filed for Social Security.

For the spouse of the worker (Spousal Retirement Benefits):

Based on their spouse's employment history, spouses who didn't work or didn't accrue enough credits to be eligible for Social Security on their own can begin receiving spousal retirement benefits at age 62. A spouse's benefit will be lowered if they apply for benefits before attaining full retirement age, much like when one applies for benefits on their own record. The maximum spousal benefit is equal to half the amount to which the spouse would otherwise be entitled at full retirement age.

(ii) Disability Benefits (Social Security Disability Insurance or SSDI).

SSDI is a federally financed program for those who are unable to work due to a disability that is anticipated to keep them out of work for at least a year. The SSDI program will provide benefits to them and certain family members. As mentioned above, people receiving SSDI benefits for two years will be automatically eligible for Medicare health insurance Part A and Part B.

As of 2022, the typical monthly SSDI benefit is between $800 and $1,800, but it can be as high as $3,000+ depending on several factors, including how long the applicant worked and their wage history. These amounts are adjusted yearly based on Social Security's calculation formulas. You can estimate your loved one's monthly benefits using the SSA's online benefits calculator by visiting www.ssa.gov.

(iii) Survivors Benefits.

The earliest a widow or widower can start receiving their survivor's benefit is when they are 60. The payout will be less if they apply before their full retirement age. If their benefit is more than their survivor's benefit, they may switch to their benefit whenever they become eligible between age 62 and 70.

The spousal benefit and the spousal survivor benefit may be received by those who were married for ten years or longer, even if they have divorced, as long as they have not remarried. However, the rules can be very complicated, so carefully review them by visiting Social Security's website (www.ssa.gov).

(iv) Supplemental Benefits (Supplemental Security Income or SSI).

If your parents' primary source of income is their Social Security benefits, which they acquired via lower-paying employment, they may be eligible for Supplemental Security Income (SSI). SSI supplements your parent's existing Social Security retirement income, resulting in a potentially larger monthly payment from the Social Security Administration. Seniors and those with disabilities can receive monthly payments through the SSI program to supplement their earnings.

Because SSI is a needs-based service, applicants must prove their eligibility by showing their lack of assets and income. In other words, SSI is reserved for individuals with extremely limited assets and very low monthly income (as of 2022, generally less than $2,000 in assets for individuals and $3,000 for couples, and less than $800 per month in income for individuals or less than $1,200 per month in income for couples).

People eligible for SSI are typically assumed also to be eligible for other needs-based benefits and services, such as the Supplemental Nutrition Assistance Program (SNAP) and Medicaid. Check Social Security's website to obtain the most recent SSI income eligibility requirements to see if your parent qualifies.

4. **The Administration on Aging (AoA)** (https://acl.gov/about-acl/administration-aging)

The AoA oversees a wide range of national initiatives and services for seniors, such as free health insurance guidance, support with legal matters, protection against elder abuse, and aid with long-term patient care.

A network of locally based organizations known as Aging and Disability Resource Centers (ADRCs) and Area Agencies on Aging (AAAs), which provides in-person and online assistance in accessing these programs and services, is also under the control of the AoA.

Volunteers and professionals with knowledge of services for elders and family caregivers work at AAAs. They may help you with benefits application preparation, collection of supporting materials, and walking you through particular eligibility criteria.

5. Department of Veterans Affairs (VA) (va.gov)

The United States government may be able to provide your elderly parent with a number of benefits if they served in the military or are the remaining spouse of a veteran. For example, the VA provides health care, long-term disability payments, pensions, burial benefits, and other benefits for qualified veterans and their accompanying family members.

Finding a veteran's discharge papers (also known as DD Form 214) is the best place to start, but prepare for time-consuming application and approval procedures. The VA uses this form to determine a veteran's discharge category or removal from active service in the armed forces, which is a crucial prerequisite for most VA benefits.

6. The Americans with Disabilities Act National Network (https://adata.org/factsheet/aging-and-ada)

The Americans with Disabilities Act (ADA) is a civil rights law that prohibits discrimination against disabled individuals in all spheres of public life, including employment, public transportation, federal and state government programs, telecommunications, public accommodations, and commercial facilities. The ADA National Network was established by the Department of Health and Human Services to disseminate data, briefings, and free publications on the laws allowing disabled people access to all areas of public life.

Knowing your parent's rights under the ADA can be helpful if age-related, and other disabilities prevent them from continuing to work. For example, certain ADA rights require workplaces to provide accommodations to enable your parent to work longer. While this may be a non-issue for the aging parents who are no longer working, it may be helpful for those who are still working.

7. **MedlinePlus / The National Institutes of Health (NIH)** (medlineplus.gov)

Seniors frequently take multiple prescription and over-the-counter medications for various medical issues. Therefore, you must understand your loved one's health situation and prescription schedule as a caregiver.

A component of the National Institutes of Health (NIH), the National Library of Medicine, manages MedlinePlus, a vast online collection of knowledge about medical disorders, diagnostic procedures, and each medication authorized by the Food and Drug Administration (FDA). Consumers may use this database to look for information about pharmaceuticals, including active components, uses, dosage suggestions, specific warnings, side effects, and interactions, in addition to understanding age-related illnesses and healthy living. Furthermore, MedlinePlus provides thorough information on dietary supplements and herbal therapies.

8. **State Long-Term Care Ombudsman Programs** (TheConsumerVoice.org/get_help)

Every state, the District of Columbia, Puerto Rico, and Guam runs an ombudsman program to assist long-term care (LTC) individuals and their families in understanding their legal rights. A full-time LTC ombudsman oversees a staff of employees and volunteers for each program.

These people pay visits to patients in long-term care facilities, look into and handle grievances, fight for high-quality treatment, and inform clients and their families of their legal rights.

∾

Local and Community Resources

Aside from national government programs supporting seniors, please also research local organizations and community resources that help the elderly and their caregivers.

Transportation

Getting your aging parent from point A to point B can be very time-consuming, especially if they can no longer drive, take public transportation independently, and depend on others for all their transportation. Find local transportation programs in your area. You can Google the following search terms:

- Senior Ride Free Program in my area
- Free Lyft and Uber rides for seniors
- Dial-a-ride for Seniors near me
- AARP Uber Discount

General Activity/Social Interaction

The following is a list of locations to take your aging loved one for a free or low-cost, stress-free outing:

- Senior Centers
- Public libraries
- Churches/Places of Worship
- Shopping Centers/Malls
- Parks
- Museums that offer free or discounted fees for seniors

Senior Centers in particular offer reduced-cost services including meal programs, enrichment classes, field trips, craft and exercise workshops, and free legal services. My mom learned how to speak Spanish and quilt through these programs, which gave her entirely new outlets to express herself and socialize with other seniors.

Legal Services

We all know legal services can be expensive, particularly for seniors living on a fixed income. Fortunately, community and non-profit organizations offer free or sliding-scale legal assistance. Research the following search terms to find available free or low costs legal services for seniors in your area:

- Legal Aid
- Legal Services for Older Americans Program
- Community legal services for seniors
- Pro Bono programs
- National Disability Rights Network (NDRN)

Also, if you work for a company, your benefits may include an employer-sponsored group legal service that may cover your aging parents.

Food and Nutrition Programs

One of the biggest challenges for aging people and their caregivers is getting three healthy meals on the table daily amidst a million other things to manage. You can research the following search terms to see what free or low-cost meal options may be available in your area:

- Senior food programs near me
- Free food for seniors near me
- Food banks near me (you can visit feedingamerica.org to find local food banks)
- Senior center meal programs near me
- Meals on Wheels (mealsonwheelsamerica.org)

- Senior food pantries near me (these locations let seniors get free groceries)
- Free home food delivery for seniors
- Commodity Supplemental Food Program (CSFP)- a federal food program for eligible low-income seniors 60+
- Supplemental Nutrition Assistance Program (SNAP)-nutrition benefits for low-income families
- Senior Farmers' Market Nutrition Program (SFMNP)-provides low-income seniors access to locally grown fruits, vegetables, honey, and herbs.

Adult Day Care Programs

Adult daycare programs offer an excellent care choice for elderly individuals with varying levels of need by providing a range of activities, help, supervision, and services. More than 260,000 senior customers and their families are supported by more than 5,000 adult daycare programs in the United States.

Adult daycare programs may offer caregivers a much-needed break while offering elders the chance to interact with peers and lessen the loneliness and isolation many face.

Research shows that older individuals who visit these programs lead healthier lives. According to a 2017 study published in The Gerontologist, participants in adult day care programs, especially those with dementia and other cognitive impairments, benefited in terms of their physical, social, psychological, and behavioral well-being. Note- Medicaid often covers all related costs for these services, which is another huge plus.

Respite Care Services

Respite care is temporary replacement care that offers caregivers temporary relief from their duties. This option involves bringing your aging parent to stay for a few nights in a facility where they provide all meals and required care on a per-night basis (similar to a hotel, but for seniors, with built-in caregivers provided!).

Short-term overnight services are provided by some senior residential communities and assisted living facilities. Some long-term care institutions reserve a certain number of beds exclusively for short-term respite stays.

This option can be a terrific stress reliever for caregivers who must travel out of town but want to ensure their loved one always has access to help.

Research and sign contracts with a few of these facilities ahead of time so you can place your loved one there if needed with just a little advanced notice.

Online Resources for Seniors and Caregivers

For Seniors

In addition to the government and local programs and resources, many other online organizations focus on supporting seniors and their caregivers. Here are a few examples:

- AARP (aarp.org) - This well-known elder advocacy group offers information for seniors and their family caregivers. There are many informative articles across multiple subject matters important to seniors and their caregivers.
- Alzheimer's Association (alz.org) - Visit this association's website to learn how to recognize

Alzheimer's and other dementias and get assistance for caregivers.

- Parkinson's Foundation (parkinson.org) - This national organization's mission is to improve life for people with Parkinson's disease by improving care and supporting research for a cure.
- National Elder Law Foundation (nelf.org) - The website of this organization offers a function that allows you to locate a qualified elder law practitioner near you.
- Global Coalition on Aging (globalcoalitiononaging.com) - This organization creates projects to address global aging issues through innovative commercial solutions and public policies.
- Benefits Checkup (benefitscheckup.org) - This is the most extensive online service in the country for connecting older individuals and those with disabilities to benefits. They make it simple by checking for eligibility. Then, they point you in the right direction for applying online or contacting a benefits consultant.
- Aging with Dignity (agingwithdignity.org) - This organization serves the rights of the elderly, disabled, and mentally ill, safeguarding their human dignity in times of severe illness.
- Love for Our Elders (loveforourelders.org) - This service finds volunteers who write letters to seniors and facilitates in-person volunteering events.
- Elder Helpers (elderhelpers.org) - This online service matches screened and trained volunteers with seniors who need help.
- Aging Life Care Association (aginglifecare.org) - This organization provides information on geriatric care managers, usually nurses or social workers, who

specialize in helping families figure out ways to meet their senior loved ones' needs. It's like hiring a "professional relative" to help figure things out.

- Eldercare Locator (www.eldercare.acl.gov) - This nationwide information and referral service assists users across various problems affecting seniors. The Locator is a trusted resource for older adults and people with disabilities looking for information and resources essential to their well-being and independence.

∽

Online Resources Based in Canada

- The Alzheimer Society of Canada (https://alzheimer.ca/en) - Their local chapters directly support persons afflicted by the illness and their caretakers.
- The Canadian Hospice Palliative Care Association (CHPCA.net) - This organization provides information about care support across Canada.
- Comfort Life (comfortlife.ca) - This comprehensive resource covers all options for retirement living across Canada.

∽

Online Resources Based in the United Kingdom

- AgeUK (ageuk.org.uk) - This UK-based organization works with and on behalf of older people to advocate for their needs, wants, and rights.

- Alzheimer's Society of the UK (https://www.
  alzheimers.org.uk/) - This UK organization provides
  support and a force for change for anyone affected by
  dementia.

For Caregivers

In addition to resources aimed at assisting seniors, there are
also many resources focused on helping the caregivers who
care for their aging family members. Here are a few examples
of these resource sites:

- Adult Children of Aging Parents (acapcommunity.org)
  - This group offers information, resources, and support
  to adult children who are caregivers for their aging
  parents. They provide education, host events, and have
  several local physical chapters for caregivers to connect
  and share information in person.
- Caring Community (caringcommunity.org) - Provided
  by the National Hospice and Palliative Care
  Organization, this website has various resources for
  caregivers and senior families, including publications,
  advocacy, and support.
- Family Caregiver Alliance (caregiver.org) - This
  organization's mission is to improve family caregivers'
  quality of life and those they care for.
- National Alliance for Caregiving (caregiving.org) - This
  organization is focused on improving the quality of life
  of family caregivers and their patients through
  advocacy, innovation, and research.
- Caring Info (caringinfo.org) - This organization helps
  patients and caregivers better understand serious

illnesses and end-of-life care and services, allowing them to make informed decisions.

- Caregiver Action (caregiveraction.org) - This organization is dedicated to enhancing the lives of the more than 90 million Americans who provide care for family members who suffer from debilitating illnesses, chronic conditions, disabilities, or the frailties of old age.
- Next Step In Care (nextstepincare.org) - This resource gives simple instructions to assist family caregivers and medical professionals in collaborating closely to plan and carry out safe transitions for very sick or chronically ill patients.
- A Better Balance (abetterbalance.org) - This is a national nonprofit organization that advocates for workers who need time off work to care for themselves or their loved ones through legislative advocacy, direct free legal services, and education. They have a state-by-state "know your rights" resource where you can review your state's workplace laws that may protect caregivers. Go to https://www.abetterbal-ance.org/know-your-rights/ for more information.

~

Online Caregiver Resources Based in Canada

- Carers Canada (carerscanada.ca) - This organization is a nationwide coalition of caregivers.

∾

Online Caregiver Resources Based in the United Kingdom

- Carers UK (carersuk.org) - UK's only national membership for caregivers, this organization provides information, support, and resources to improve UK-based caregivers' lives.

∾

Mobile Apps for Caregivers

You can also explore the ever-expanding list of mobile apps designed to help caregivers. Here are a few examples:

- CaringBridge (caringbridge.org) - An app that keeps track of your loved one's whereabouts and connects to family caregivers and supporters (for iOS users).
- Medisafe (medisafe.com) - An app that keeps track of your parent's prescriptions by providing reminders, details on interactions, and other helpful information (For iOS and Android users).
- PainScale (painscale.com) - An app that assists you in tracking and managing the pain of an elderly loved one. A pain, medication, exercise, mood, and sleep quality diary can create a report that can be shared with medical specialists (for Android and iOS users).

- Sanvello (sanvello.com) - An app that is designed specifically for caregivers who are stressed out. Quick activities, specific goals, and community support can help caregivers deal with the stresses of caring for elderly parents (for Android and iOS users).

This is just a partial list of the vast resources for the elderly and their caregivers. Review this list, research other sites on the Internet for general caregiver information, and look into the available services.

∼

Resources and Tips for Long-Distance Caregivers

Taking care of an aging loved one is hard. But taking care of them from a distance has its own set of unique challenges. Here are some tips if you find yourself in this category of long-distance family caregivers:

Organize a family meeting. Discuss your aging loved one's care needs with your family members and determine how to divide caregiving needs. It is important to set expectations from the beginning so everyone is on the same page and contributes in their own way. Those family members who are long-distance can help with remote tasks, such as offering financial help, helping to organize and pay bills, coordinating medical appointments, or arranging transportation and meal services to be delivered.

Visit your loved one. Although you may figure out a good plan to help remotely most of the time, ensure that you make the trips to visit in person. This will strengthen the bond between you and your loved one, help create cherished memories and prevent any regrets down the road. In addition, a visit may offer encouragement and respite to a sibling caregiver.

Know the neighbors. It's a good idea to get to know your aging loved one's neighbors and introduce yourself to them on your next visit. Compile a list of phone numbers so you have extra eyes and ears in case of any emergency. Jot this down in the *Emergency Contact List* in the *Master Caregiver Checklist* in the Appendix.

Make an emergency plan. Create a plan in the event of emergencies and email it to the rest of the family so everyone has a copy.

Use Smart Technology. Certain gadgets help caregivers remotely monitor what's happening in their aging parent's home. Things such as Wi-Fi-enabled security cameras, smart doorbells, smart thermostats, and smart speaker devices let you keep your eyes and ears on your loved one from the comfort of your smartphone.

These "smart" tech tools are your "secret weapons" that enable you to watch over your parents and have more peace of mind without being physically tethered to their location. These will prove to be huge time savers if incorporated into your routine. While available, go to www.cynthiakaye.com to get a list of recommended smart gadgets and tools and links to where you can find them.

Create a team of outsourced help. Work to create a team of hired paid caregivers and other helpers (like house cleaners and handypersons) to cover the various needs where there is a gap.

Get your parent a cell phone. Set up a cell phone for your loved one in a way that makes it as simple to use as possible. For example, remove all unnecessary apps on the mobile phone home page and put shortcut icons with photos of you and other family members to make it easy for your loved one just to press the photo to call you. If your parent is a bit more tech-savvy, install apps they might enjoy- such as simple mobile games (solitaire, Candy Crush, etc.) and potentially even some social media apps like Facebook, YouTube, and Tiktok to provide them with some entertainment throughout the day. Also, show them how to text message if they are able.

Consider alternative living arrangements. If they're no longer able to live independently, it may be time to find more suitable living arrangements for your loved one. Refer to Chapter 6 for an overview of different living arrangements, including assisted living and skilled nursing facilities, depending on the level of care your loved one needs.

Consider moving closer. I know this may not be feasible in many situations, but long-distance caregivers may consider if it makes more sense to continue to give care remotely or if they can manage to move closer to make it easier on themselves.

"Learn What Resources are Available" Summary Checklist

Reminders from this chapter:

1. Familiarize yourself with the various government programs for seniors, such as Medicare, Medicaid, and Social Security, to see if your aging loved one is eligible.
2. Spend time reviewing other senior and caregiver resources provided through various local and community organizations, such as adult day care programs and other community resources, to assist your senior's daily life.

3. Review the education and support provided by many online resources such as AARP.

4. Apply for any applicable programs to start the process and be diligent about following up. Government benefits are hard to get and easy to lose if you miss a filing or a deadline for a response. So, keep organized and stay on top of all deadlines.

5. Review the tips on being a long-distance caregiver if that applies to your situation.

Obtaining practical knowledge of all available resources will mean the difference between being overwhelmed and feeling supported. Across the country and globally, resource groups that assist and empower seniors and their caregivers offer advice, support, and tools to lighten your caregiving load. Remember, you are not alone.

4

EVALUATE HOW TO PAY FOR CARE

Now that you know the available resources at your disposal, the next step is determining how your loved one will pay for their care. This will enable you to make informed decisions about the care plan in light of the budget you have to work with. Unfortunately, the cost of medical care can be staggering. Even if your loved one has diligently accumulated their life savings, these costs can quickly drain large sums of money.

∼

Paying for Long-Term Care

Costs to care for an aging person can be exorbitant. Therefore, a huge stressor for families is how to cover these caregiving costs, medical costs, and the ever-increasing general cost of living.

There are several options to pay for care. These care expenses can vary widely depending on your financial situation, the services you utilize, and whether care is provided at home, in an assisted living facility, or in a skilled nursing facility. The reality is that many families pay for these expenses with a patchwork of various funding sources, including personal savings, assistance from family members, government assistance programs, and private financing options.

Let's look at some of these options:

Personal Savings and Assistance from Family Members

These are funds that directly come out of your family's pocket. Many seniors initially contribute financially to their care. They can use their savings, money from pensions or other retirement accounts, income from stocks and bonds, or money from selling a house.

A 2021 AARP research showed the stark reality that family caregivers face today. According to one of their studies, nearly 8 in 10 family caregivers face a significant financial strain, spending 26% of their total income annually on out-of-pocket costs related to caregiving.

While family members and friends may initially offer free personal care and other assistance, such as transportation or meal preparation, this family assistance is often not long-term and usually not enough to cover the aging loved one's increasing needs. Therefore, the next step may be asking for financial support from various family members to help create a pool of funds to hire outsourced helpers and provide care.

However, for families who can't afford to give this additional financial support, or once the aging loved one's needs increase to the point of exceeding or exhausting the family's financial ability, family caregivers need to look elsewhere for additional sources of funding.

Government Assistance Programs

Government assistance programs are one of the first places to look for additional funding to supplement the family's ability to cover caregiving costs. These programs are designed to assist elderly and vulnerable populations who genuinely need help. There is no shame or harm in looking into these programs. They are not charity or a handout; instead, they are often benefits that your parent may have paid into their entire working lives- and are entitled to receive now that they need the assistance.

Medicare and Medicaid

We discussed Medicare and Medicaid in Chapter 3. As discussed, there are many benefits that your loved one may qualify for under these programs. However, eligibility is state-specific and depends on individual circumstances, so we can't describe the particular benefits here. Therefore, research your specific state at https://www.medicaid.gov/state-overviews/index.html and https://www.medicareresources.org/states to determine which benefits your loved one is eligible for.

Think of Medicare as your loved one's primary medical insurance once they reach 65 and meet all eligibility requirements. Think of Medicaid as additional coverage that supplements Medicare for eligible low-income individuals.

If your aging parent is eligible for Medicaid, an entire world of free to low-cost benefits opens up. This is worth looking into closely and discussing with an eldercare attorney to determine eligibility and Medicaid planning strategies. Remember that even if your parent does not initially qualify for Medicaid, they may later be eligible as they spend down their assets.

Research what expenses Medicare and Medicaid will cover in your parent's circumstance and related eligibility and application processes by visiting their websites at https://www.medicare.gov/ and https://www.medicaid.gov/ for more details.

Social Security Benefits

We also previously covered Social Security benefits, which can provide significant funding to qualified individuals based on their different programs. Whether it's retirement, disability, supplemental or spousal benefits, it is imperative to research and verify that your loved one is getting all the benefits they are entitled to.

One note on disability benefits, also known as Social Security Disability Insurance (SSDI): If your aging parent has not yet reached retirement age (62) and has a disability, you may consider helping them apply for SSDI.

SSDI allows applicants to get their Social Security retirement payments before retirement age. However, these SSDI applications can take a very long process, requiring a lot of paperwork, medical records, and multiple appeals and hearings. Therefore, it would be wise to get a good disability lawyer to help represent you on a contingency fee basis (in other words, no upfront out-of-pocket costs to the client).

Check out free online services such as www.Atticus.com or www.nosscr.com to get matched with a reputable Social Security disability attorney to help with your case.

The Social Security Administration offers an expedited SSDI application review process known as "compassionate allowances" to enable severely ill applicants to receive disability benefits more promptly. This includes people suffering from certain severe conditions such as Alzheimer's disease and multiple other severe medical conditions.

You can get more specific eligibility information on Social Security's website (ssa.gov) or by calling the SSA at 1-800-772-1213.

Program of All-Inclusive Care for the Elderly (PACE)

This Medicare/Medicaid program offers care and services to seniors who would otherwise require care in a nursing home. But it's only available in some states. PACE enables most eligible individuals to stay in their homes rather than transfer to long-term care facilities. Call 1-877-267-2323 to find out more. You can check the website at http://www.pace4you.org/ to learn more.

Program for Assistance with State Health Insurance (SHIP)

This is a federal initiative made available in every state that offers advice and support to individuals and their families on issues relating to Medicare and Medicare supplemental insurance (Medigap). Go to the website (https://www.shiphelp.org/) to contact a SHIP counselor in your state.

U.S. Department of Veterans Affairs (VA)

Check with the VA or contact the VA medical facility closest to you to see if a member of your family or a relative qualifies for veterans' benefits.

Please call 1-877-222-8387 or check out the Veterans Health Administration website (https://www.va.gov/health/). It has a page on Veterans Affairs Caregiver Support describing the VA's Caregiver Support Program that offers services and support to eligible family caregivers who look after veterans enrolled in the VA health care system. See caregiver.va.gov for more information.

National Council on Aging (NCOA)

BenefitsCheckUp is a free service offered by NCOA. You can use this tool to locate federal and state assistance programs that could benefit your loved one. You can view a list of potential benefit programs to investigate after giving some general information about the person who needs care. These programs can cover prescription medications, heating costs, housing, nutrition programs, and legal services. To utilize this service, you are not required to provide your name, address, or Social Security number. Call 1-571-527-3900 to learn more about Benefits-CheckUp or go to benefitscheckup.org.

Private Financing Options

Long-term care insurance, reverse mortgages, and annuities are a few examples of private financing possibilities. Of course, the optimal solution for a particular person will depend on many variables, such as age, health, personal savings, and the likelihood of needing care.

Let's look at the options:

Long-Term Care Insurance

Long-term care insurance helps cover the cost of care once the insured policyholder suffers from a chronic medical condition that affects their ability to perform certain basic activities of daily living (ADLs- more to come on these in later chapters).

For caregivers, here's what you need to look out for when it comes to long-term care insurance:

Ask your parent or other family members if they have already purchased a long-term care insurance policy. When an adult child assumes the role of caregiver for their aging parent, it is generally too late to consider buying a new long-term care insurance policy. These policies are best purchased when the insured is younger and healthier (usually in their 50s or early 60s) when the insurance payments are more affordable. If your parent didn't buy this years ago, it's probably best to move forward and look at other options.

If your parent does have long-term care insurance coverage, your next step is to get a copy of the insurance policy contract and read every word carefully. Outline the eligibility requirements, the coverage terms and limits, and how to contact the insurance company to initiate a claim. There may be deductible periods and fine print to review- these are all important to study carefully.

Then proceed and open a claim to start the process. Depending on what your parent selected, these policies can cover a wide range of services and reimburse you for costs associated with in-home care or care at assisted living or skilled nursing facilities. Each coverage will detail the maximum daily or monthly dollar amount covered- so pay close attention to those details and follow their application instructions to a tee.

Figure out the most strategic time to submit a claim to maximize the policy's coverage and benefits. For example, suppose the policy only covers four years of care total, and your aging parent is still relatively in good health but is just starting to need assistance. In that case, you may want to wait and "save" those coverage years for a later period when your parent gets older and may need more help.

But, on the other hand, you don't want to hold out and wait too long to start a claim, as any unused amounts of the insurance benefits at the time of the insured's death will be forfeited. This is what happened to my father's policy. During his last year of life, we used about $50,000 of his long-term care policy to help pay for his in-home caregivers. By the time he passed away, he still had over $300,000 of long-term care insurance benefits that he didn't use. We had to forfeit that remaining balance since we didn't spend it down.

Reverse Mortgages

A reverse mortgage is a unique type of house loan that enables a homeowner to turn a portion of the home's ownership value into cash.

Unlike a conventional house loan, there are no repayment obligations until the home is sold, the borrower stops using it as their primary residence, or they pass away.

To qualify for a reverse mortgage, your loved one must be 62 or older; there are no income or medical restrictions. The loan amount can be used for any purpose, including long-term care, and is tax-free. However, you must first use the money to settle debts, such as a mortgage.

Consider these pros and cons of reverse mortgages:

PROS:

- It provides steady income in your parent's later years. Reverse mortgages may be a great option for retirees who have accumulated significant equity in their houses but little in cash savings or investments. With the help of a reverse mortgage, you can convert an otherwise illiquid asset into cash that you can use for long-term care costs.
- It allows them to stay at home. Your loved one can continue to live in the property and still receive cash from it, so you don't have to sell it to liquidate the asset. This eliminates worrying about the labor-intensive

process of downsizing or being priced out of their community.

- Your parent will pay off their current mortgage. A reverse mortgage can be obtained even if the house isn't completely paid off. You can pay off an existing mortgage with the money from a reverse mortgage. This makes money available to use for other expenses.
- The monthly income is tax-free. The IRS regards the money from a reverse mortgage as a loan advance rather than as income. Therefore, as opposed to other retirement income like distributions from a 401(k) or IRA, the cash flow from a reverse mortgage is not taxed.
- Never owe more than the home is worth. If there is concern that your loved one's home value may drop in the future, then getting a reverse mortgage lets them cash in based on the higher value of their home today. Even if the home value falls below the loan amount, your loved one's heirs will not be responsible for that difference.

CONS:

- The heirs' inheritance can be affected. The family's generational wealth, which includes home ownership, is impacted. A reverse mortgage typically necessitates the sale of the house to pay off the debt at the time of the homeowner's death.
- Possible foreclosure. To be eligible for a reverse mortgage, one must pay property taxes, homeowners' insurance, HOA dues, and other house ownership costs. Additionally, your loved one must spend most of the year residing in the house as their primary residence. This means that one runs the risk of

defaulting on the reverse mortgage and losing the
house to foreclosure if they fall behind on these
payments.

- Other retirement benefits may be impacted. Even
though a reverse mortgage is not taxable income, it
may still affect your parent's eligibility for other need-
based government programs like Medicaid. This is
because such payments from the reverse mortgage
may still count as "income" and make your parent's
income too high for certain programs.
- Variable interest rates. Most reverse mortgages have
variable interest rates, meaning that during the loan's
life, the interest rate that determines how much is
added to the loan total each month changes.
- Potential home repairs. Repairs may need to be made
to the house if it's in poor condition in order to be
eligible for a reverse mortgage.

Annuities

To pay for long-term care services, your aging parent could also
consider an annuity contract with an insurance provider.

With an annuity, you pay a set amount of money to the insurance company today or over time to get a lump sum payment or
income stream in the future.

Let's look at some pros and cons of annuities:

PROS:

- Your parent gets guaranteed and regular income. An
annuity can offer guaranteed income either
immediately or gradually. The recipient's overall
income from sources like Social Security or an IRA can
be supplemented by this guaranteed income.

Depending on the type of annuity, your parent may get monthly, quarterly, or annual income installments instead of a lump sum.

- The rate of interest is fixed. With a fixed annuity, you can guarantee an interest rate, such as 3% annually. This allows one to better predict how much cash flow will come in with a fixed interest rate (the higher the interest rate, the more cash flow).

- Tax-Deferred contributions. The money contributed to a tax-deferred annuity isn't taxed until after the annuitant retires. Before they begin receiving annuity payments, taxes are not due. Therefore, they're exempt from paying taxes on any capital gains as long as the money is not touched while in an annuity.

- Unlimited contributions. Regardless of your loved one's income level or sources of income, there is no cap on the amount of after-tax money they can invest in an annuity.

- Investment options. For a set period of time, fixed annuities offer a predetermined rate of return. Various investment options, such as stocks, bonds, and money market instruments, are included in variable annuities. These options change in value in response to market conditions.

CONS:

- Fees and commissions. Certain annuities include fees. These can range from 2% to 3% annually, which can be higher than other investment types.

- Money is tied up. Annuities may limit the ability to access one's money. For example, most annuities permit the owner to withdraw a specified amount of money, often 10% annually, without paying a surrender fee during the surrender period (usually six to eight years). However, the rest of the money in the annuity is not accessible.

- Fluctuating returns. If you have a variable or indexed annuity, the cash value can fluctuate according to the state of the market. As a result, your parent's cash flow from the annuity may become more unpredictable. To offset this risk, you can purchase a fixed-rate annuity.
- Surrender charges. The insurer may levy significant surrender fees if an annuity owner wants to withdraw money from the annuity before a set amount of time has passed (usually six to eight years, but occasionally more).
- Penalty taxes. A 10% early withdrawal penalty may also be applied to any money withdrawn if the annuity owner is under the age of 59.

Be sure to check with your financial planner and/or accountant as the terms of these and other investment products vary on a case-by-case basis.

~

Additional Funding Sources

Many families need every source of additional funding possible in order to manage the high costs of caregiving.

Here are some ideas to explore:

Home Sharing

If your parent has any extra space in their home, one option to cut expenses is to find a roommate or housemate for them. Managing the costs of living alone can become very challenging as people age. Your elderly loved ones can reduce costs and fight loneliness by sharing their home.

There are various advantages to having your parent share their home with a vetted roommate. Shared housing can simplify and improve senior living, from lowering costs to increasing companionship.

It also provides extra peace of mind knowing that there are an extra pair of eyes and ears at the home when you're not there. Having someone always in the home provides security and comfort for you and your aging parent.

There are several services where you can look for a roommate or housemate for your parent. Home-sharing services like Airbnb.com and SeniorHomeShares.com can both do the job. Just be sure to familiarize yourself with the rules for each service and follow them carefully to avoid running afoul of any applicable local home-sharing laws and regulations.

SeniorHomeShares.com is a nice option since it is designed for senior citizens. They are a means for seniors to manage their finances while living securely and having opportunities to make friends.

Senior Home pairs senior citizens looking for safe, affordable accommodation with others on fixed incomes who have extra space in their homes. High housing expenses can lead seniors to spend less on necessities like food and medicine. Thus, an option like this can be life-changing.

While Airbnb is not focused on pairing seniors with seniors, it can also be an effective option for finding nice roommates for your aging parent.

You just have to be more involved in creating a clear room listing and description and specify that you are looking for someone to stay in your elderly parent's home.

While you need to be careful not to violate anti-discrimination rules, you can indicate the preferred gender of the roommate if it's the same gender as your aging parent. Check out the Airbnb platform rules for more details.

I set up one of the bedrooms in my parents' townhome on Airbnb starting when they were in their mid-70s. The primary reason was to give them more companionship and social connection, as they tended to be isolated homebodies.

Giving them a new "job" as "temporary landlords" for the various month-long stays that came through Airbnb was a Godsend and had many positive outcomes for my parents.

In addition to the additional income for the bedroom rent, many of the Airbnb "guests" became very close friends of my parents and our entire family. They are some of our dearest friends to this day and hold a very special place in our hearts.

Another DIY option is to use Craigslist.com and write up your own "Seeking Roommate for my Elderly Parent" listing. See the Appendix for a sample of such a listing to get some initial ideas.

Once the COVID-19 pandemic hit, we temporarily stopped our Airbnb bedroom to avoid the comings and goings of the monthly guests.

We switched to looking for a long-term tenant for that bedroom on Craigslist. We found a wonderful lady in her 60s who has become a dear friend and an honorary member of our family.

Having her there with my mother in her 80s gives me peace of mind when I cannot be there, knowing that my mom doesn't feel alone. I can't recommend this enough if arranging a house-mate for your parent is possible.

Downsizing

Helping your aging parent downsize their home may be another way to access more funds. However, planning, effort, and time are required when downsizing. It entails decluttering the present home, giving away or selling unnecessary belongings, listing the home for sale, and relocating. While some people enlist the aid of professionals, others turn to friends and family for assistance.

One of the main motives for downsizing is to save money. Finding a more affordable home is a relatively straightforward approach to quickly boosting finances and improving your loved one's financial ability to pay for their caregiving and medical needs.

Here are some other advantages of downsizing:

- Lower Mortgage. A new home with a smaller monthly mortgage can provide the budget with breathing room. The monthly savings from this can go toward caregiving and medical expenses.
- Less Cleaning and Maintenance. There's a trend that older Americans are spending more on home renovations (about $117 billion in 2017). That's a lot of money that could be saved by downsizing to a smaller and potentially newer home that requires minimal maintenance and cleaning.
- Lower Utility Bills. Lower utility expenses result from fewer rooms and smaller spaces. You could also save

much more if you move into a house with new
windows or energy-saving appliances.

Of course, the decision to downsize is a major personal decision that belongs to your parent, not you. While this may be a
delicate subject, open communication, sensitivity, and empathy
will go a long way. Perhaps you can enlist some friends or
family, especially those who have downsized, to help socialize
the idea with your parent. Eventually, your parent may be open
and willing to make that move with enough supporters.

Community or Work-Sponsored Benefits

If you are a current employee, determine whether your
employer offers family caregiver benefits. You will want to
know if there are any benefits that you can utilize to reduce
stress and help support your needs as a caregiver.

One example of a company-sponsored benefit is the Bright
Horizons Back-up Care Program. When temporary distur-
bances in elder caregiving arrangements prohibit one from
completing work duties, the program offers the caregiver
backup care. Each company may provide different levels of
benefits, so you'll need to check what your company may offer
in terms of the number of hours provided and any co-payments
charged to you. You can learn more about it at brighthorizon-
s.com and check in with your HR and benefits department. You
may even suggest it as a benefit if it isn't currently offered.

"Evaluate How to Pay for Care" Summary Checklist.

Reminders from this chapter:

1. Research and understand the various funding sources to cover your aging parent's care needs.
2. Once you've applied for government benefits and researched private financing options, explore additional funding sources such as home sharing or downsizing.
3. Check with your employer for caregiver benefits, such as backup care services.

As discussed, caregiving and its accompanying costs can be exorbitant. In addition, the demand for long-term care will rise sharply as the U.S. population ages and millions of baby boomers enter their later years. As a result, it is becoming a national crisis to figure out how to support caregivers financially as more and more people are being thrust into this challenging situation.

Don't despair. You have a number of options to help pay for care. There may be some legwork and perseverance to apply and qualify, but the important thing to remember is that there are options. You're not alone in this struggle. Most families are in a similar boat and are researching and relying on various funding options to get through this caregiving season. Just take it one day at a time and one resource application at a time- and don't give up.

DECIDE ON LIVING ARRANGEMENTS AND RELATED CARE PLANS

I t is time to research the best living arrangements and related care options within your family's budget. Knowing your family's various financial resources and funds will help in this endeavor.

~

Living Arrangements

Aging is a part of everyone's reality. But sometimes, adult children may not realize how aging will affect their parents as the effects of aging may be gradual. For example, if your parents are in good health and live independently, you might not notice significant changes or have serious worries. But it becomes different when aging is more advanced and if there are declining health conditions involved. Then, long-term care may be required.

In this light, we consider living arrangements. Every family usually has the moment when the adult children must determine where their elderly parents should live to ensure their well-being.

Do they reside alone? Do they live close to you, your siblings, or other family members? Do they want to stay in their current house, or do they need to move to a facility?

All of these issues should be thoroughly discussed with your aging parent. If they are still of sound mind and can competently decide on the matter, their wishes on where they reside should be carefully heard and considered. But, of course, every situation will differ, and you will have to consider your parent's particular set of facts to figure out the best solution.

Let's review the most common senior living arrangements:

Nursing homes (also called skilled nursing facilities or convalescent homes)

Nursing homes offer various medical and personal care services for seniors suffering from severe, debilitating physical and/or cognitive health conditions. Compared to most assisted living homes, their services place a greater emphasis on medical care. These services frequently include nursing care, 24-hour supervision, three meals daily, and assistance with ADLs. Additional rehabilitation services include speech, occupational, and physical therapy.

After leaving the hospital, some patients spend a brief period in a nursing home. The majority of patients return home after they have healed. However, some remain permanently because of enduring health issues that necessitate continuing care and supervision.

There are many strong feelings one way or another about nursing homes but nobody can argue that they serve an important role in society. There are situations in which the nursing home is the only viable option for many families. It's helpful to understand some of the pros and cons of nursing homes:

PROS:

- 24/7 full-time comprehensive care
- On-site support by qualified healthcare professionals
- Structured schedules and predictable routines designed to help seniors
- Community element providing social interaction to otherwise isolated seniors

CONS:

- Very expensive (and limited choices and lower quality of care for nursing homes accepting Medicaid)
- Lack of personalization and freedom- each room and bed usually look the same and the senior is generally limited to activities provided by the facility
- Confinement in close quarters with others may lead to faster spread of diseases like COVID-19
- Quality of care issues provided by overworked staff or facilities that are understaffed

Each nursing home facility will vary greatly in the various aspects of care and offerings. Researching and visiting multiple facilities will give you a much better sense of whether this could be the right choice for your loved one.

Independent Senior Living Communities

This arrangement is best suited for independent, active seniors who purchase or rent a home, apartment, or mobile home in a community of other seniors. Depending on the community, they may have access to clubhouses, gyms, and other activities.

In addition, the community may also provide a la carte house-keeping, security, laundry, transportation, and other essential amenities. The downside to these communities is that there's generally no assistance for medical care in most cases and you're on your own to find and hire your own caregivers.

Continuing Care Retirement Communities

Also known as life care communities, CCRCs provide several service levels in one area (in other words, a full continuum of care in one large community for seniors).

On one campus, CCRC's provide independent accommodations, such as apartments or houses, assisted living facilities, and skilled nursing care. Additionally, they offer meal, leisure, and healthcare services.

Where a person lives within a CCRC is based on the required degree of care services needed. For example, if your loved one can no longer live independently, they move into an assisted living facility section of the community. But occasionally, they continue to live independently while receiving in-home care. If their needs surpass what can be managed at the assisted living facilities, they can go into the skilled nursing facility within the CCRC.

Like with everything else, there are pros and cons of the CCRC option:

PROS:

- All-inclusive, full-amenity living, similar to an all-inclusive resort, where housing, meals, entertainment, and social gatherings may be built into the program
- The convenience that the CCRC will be the "last time they'll move"- they can start in independent living,

then move to assisted living, then nursing home facilities all within the CCRC

- Near-complete peace of mind for kids of aging parents because almost everything is outsourced and covered by the CCRC based on the facility and the fees charged (assuming the family has sufficient funds to cover these costs)

CONS:

- Extremely expensive- most families will find CCRCs cost-prohibitive. There are large upfront entrance fees, monthly maintenance fees, and additional a la carte fees for additional services. These all add up quickly.
- Potentially financially risky- most CCRCs require a large upfront "entrance fee" to buy into the community. This lump sum can approach half a million dollars or more in some states. If the CCRC (which is ultimately a business) is mismanaged, it could shut down and go bankrupt, in which case your loved one could lose that lump sum.
- One size may not fit all. Your parent may like one aspect of the CCRC, such as the independent living facilities, but later realize that they really don't like the assisted living area. At that point, backing out may be difficult depending on the contract terms.

Assisted Living

Seniors requiring daily care assistance but not as much assistance as a nursing home can consider assisted living. In assisted living facilities, there may be anywhere from 6 to 120 (or more) residents.

These facilities range from cozy and privately-owned residential homes with six bedrooms to large 100+ room corporation-owned facilities. In addition, there are typically some levels of care available, costing residents more.

Residents of assisted living facilities typically have their own apartments or rooms and share communal areas. The pros and cons for assisted living facilities are somewhat similar to those for nursing homes, except another "pro" for assisted living facilities is that they may have a more homey and cozy feel than a nursing home, which often has more of a hospital or institutional feel.

Numerous services are available for residents and vary from facility to facility. These may include:

- Meals (up to three per day plus snacks)
- Help with medications
- Assistance with personal care and grooming
- Incontinence care
- Round-the-clock monitoring
- Housekeeping services
- Laundry services
- Security
- On-site employees
- Social and recreational events.

Aging-In-Place (in their own home)

Despite the above options, many seniors still prefer to live and age in their own homes- known as "aging in place." Aging in place is one of the most prominent trends in senior living. In fact, according to certain polls, about 87% of seniors hope to remain in their homes for the rest of their lives.

While we understand that many want to maintain their independence and remain in their own homes, there are various pros and cons to aging in place. Here are a few of them:

PROS:

- Cost-effectiveness. Aging in place is often far less expensive than going into a facility if you can make it work. Nursing homes and assisted living facilities are both costly options. The national median cost of such facilities in the United States in 2021 was $54,000 per year ($4,500 per month). On average, a private room in a nursing home in the U.S. costs about $95,000 per year (about $8,000 per month). Some may have long-term care insurance to help offset such expenses, but many families still find the cost prohibitive.
- Familiarity. Since one stays in a neighborhood where they know their neighbors, it's a plus. Also, if your loved one has been a resident in the same house for a while, they have probably been a part of the local community where people know them.
- Easy access to outside services. With the advent of technology, it is easier for people, even elders, to take advantage of available services that make aging in place simpler. For example, if seniors struggle with performing activities like buying groceries, medicine, and cleaning, they can hire someone to help them or have them ordered online for delivery.
- Satisfaction with seeing home updates. Personalizing your home is one of the greatest pleasures of home ownership. Your parents can make all the modifications they wish to make the space more distinctively theirs. Residents of assisted living facilities are never quite able to make it as distinctly

their own space as with their own houses since
assisted living facilities are created to please as many
people as possible. So, when they stay at home, they
can benefit from all the modifications they've made to
their place.

- Freedom and comfort. I am sure that most seniors
consider this the most crucial advantage of aging in
place. For them, their highest priority is being free and
comfortable. It feels cozier to stay in your own home, a
place connected to so many special memories. You feel
more independent than if you had moved into a
facility.

CONS:

- Less quality of care. People enter nursing homes and
assisted living facilities for many reasons. They require
a degree of care that their families cannot supply on
their own. Your home won't cut it if a senior's health
worsens to the point that they must be close to a
healthcare provider at all hours of the day. They'll
require a nursing facility. Usually, it only makes sense
to age in place if there are enough family members
nearby willing to chip in and help. However, there's a
big chance they'll need to move if there aren't enough
family members who can cover the duties that staff
members in an external facility handle.
- Safety issues. When a senior falls at home alone, they
may be stuck there for hours until a family member or
in-home care provider arrives. Having someone
around who can quickly step in to help out when a
health emergency occurs can significantly affect how
safe and healthy your loved one remains in their later
senior years.

- Feelings of isolation and loneliness. The feeling of loneliness and isolation is one of the biggest disadvantages associated with aging in place. In addition to the melancholy that comes with having few to no close friends or family nearby, if your loved one doesn't put in the effort to maintain social ties, they risk developing several health issues linked to loneliness.
- A higher possibility of mental or cognitive health decline. Age-related mental and cognitive decline is inevitable. However, different people will be affected differently by it. This decline could become hazardous or unhealthy if your loved one lives alone. They might forget to take their medication or eat properly. They might disregard issues with the gas line or the electrical wiring.
- Unable to afford house upkeep. Of course, as you become older, your home will too. Aging people's homes often fall into disrepair. They might not have noticed that things are falling apart one by one—roof leaks, worn wiring in the walls, mold all around, and other stages of deterioration. Your loved one may have money, but tapping into their savings in this manner may not be ideal. There may be more essential expenses they'd like to save for.

We ended up taking care of my dad during his final years at home. This was in part because those were his wishes, and we wanted to keep him and my mom (his wife) together under the same roof. It also turned out to be more affordable and work-able for us as a family. Plus, because it was during Covid-19 when there was a slew of breakouts at nursing homes and assisted living facilities, it just seemed to make the most sense for us.

There were numerous times when we weren't sure if we could handle the growing level of care my dad needed at home. We weren't professional nurses after all. But we ultimately managed to keep him at home all the way until the end with the help of some incredible paid caregivers who helped fill in the caregiving gaps.

Senior Care Placement Referral Agencies

Families who decide to look for an assisted living facility for their loved one can look on their own or can use placement or referral agencies to look for them.

Before, these agencies were known as Assisted Living Placement Agencies. Now, they are more widely known as Assisted Living Referral Services. These are institutions that assist families in identifying the kind of assisted living residence to place their loved ones in.

These services are beneficial for people who are far away from family members who need care. Referral services significantly aid in reducing the options available. Additionally, they offer families their services at no cost. They receive a referral fee from the assisted living facility once a referred senior moves in, usually in the form of one month's rent.

Like other services, there are pros and cons to using one of these referral services. Consider them if you plan to use them now or in the future.

PROS:

- You have additional access to information about the neighborhood that you might not have otherwise had.

- They work on your behalf and take some of the pressure off when searching for suitable senior facilities by yourself.
- They can work directly with the senior living community to negotiate prices and terms.
- Rather than having to send your information to dozens of online contact forms, you can keep your information private.
- They aid in understanding how to effectively manage your finances, provide for the needs of your family members, and other helpful resources.
- They can assist you in finding facilities that fit your budget.

CONS:

- They may prioritize selling higher-priced, more luxury facilities to earn a larger referral fee (as their payment is often tied to one month's rent of the facility).
- There could be a disconnect or mismatch between the facility and the resident if the referral agency didn't facilitate direct communications before the move-in date.
- A referral agency may suggest a facility that just happens to have an opening, even if it's not a good match for your particular needs, just to fulfill those openings in their network of facilities.
- Seniors who may not have chosen an assisted living facility may feel compelled to do so by the extra pressure of competition created between these referral agencies.

～

Care Arrangements

Depending on which living arrangement your loved one ends up choosing, that will affect the type of care arrangement they will get. For example, the assisted living and skilled nursing facilities provide their own team of caregivers who come with the living arrangement. Your loved one's level of care needed will determine if you'll need to pay extra or not, depending on the facility's policies.

In contrast, independent senior living communities generally do not provide caregivers, leaving you to figure out your care plan just as you would if your loved one stayed in their own home. CCRCs have a combination of the above, depending on whether your loved one is staying in the community's independent, assisted living, or skilled nursing section.

However, the family will need to figure out the best care arrangements for seniors who decide to age in place. Here are some things to keep in mind when figuring out this important aspect of your parent's aging-in-place plan.

Home Care vs. Home Health Care

First, let's clarify the difference between home care and home health care, often shortened to "home health."

Although home care and home health care may sound alike, the services are quite different.

Home Health Care

Home health care involves medical supervision provided by licensed professionals such as registered and licensed nurses and physical or occupational therapists. They can do this through home health agencies. In some instances, they do this through hospice agencies. A doctor usually advises this type of care as part of a senior health care routine after an injury or hospitalization.

It may include the following types of services:

- Administration of prescription drugs or shots
- Medical lab tests
- Physical and occupational therapy
- Health monitoring
- Wound care

Not every senior needs home health care. Those with more severe and persistent medical problems are more likely to need these higher-level services. Some examples of seniors who may benefit from home health include:

- Seniors who have recently been released from a skilled care facility, hospital, or rehabilitation center
- Elderly individuals who require supervision following a recent drug adjustment
- Family members whose precarious health makes it unsafe for them to travel to and from doctors' offices
- Seniors losing their independence due to a general reduction in function may benefit from occupational or physical therapy

The 2020 Cost of Care Survey from Genworth Financial estimates that the monthly median cost of full-time home health care services for seniors is almost $4,500. This assumes a weekly care schedule of 44 hours. Costs for home health care vary significantly depending on location, services provided, and the degree of care needed by a senior. Note: home health care services costs are covered by Medicare if deemed medically necessary by a physician.

Home Care

Home care offers assistance for elders who require help with daily tasks. Depending on the individual's needs, care levels might range from weekly meal preparation to hourly incontinence assistance. Home care assistants can be employed directly or through agencies. They are skilled in the subtleties of senior care but are typically not qualified to offer medical services. Among the various daily duties covered by home care aides include:

- Help with ADLs
- Cleaning
- Means of transportation for doctor appointments
- Companionship
- Assistance with managing finances
- Meal preparation
- Management of medication

Many seniors aging in place can benefit from home care, from those who need just a little extra help to others who require much more assistance. Here are some examples of people who would benefit from home care:

- Seniors who require assistance with their daily activities (ADLs), including washing and using the restroom
- Those who need help with cooking, cleaning, and other domestic duties
- Seniors who feel lonely or seek company at home
- Seniors who need transportation to and from activities and medical appointments

According to Genworth, home care costs an average of $24 per hour in 2020. These costs, however, vary depending on several factors, including location, state wage regulations, and home care agency markups.

Families frequently discover that their loved ones benefit from a mix of home health and home care. While home care assistants help with daily tasks, home health providers offer more targeted and specialized medical services and therapies. You can assess your loved one's particular needs to determine the right balance between these two types of in-home caregiver services.

Hiring Caregivers Directly or Through a Caregiver Agency

Once you've decided to hire paid caregivers for your loved one, you need to evaluate the options for finding these workers. The most common paths available are going through a Home Care Agency or directly finding and hiring a caregiver. Let's look at some pros and cons of each option.

Home Care Agency PROS:

- There's a built-in pre-vetted pool of qualified workers ready to go.
- Most agencies handle all tax requirements, payroll paperwork, references, and background checks.
- Most agencies offer employee training, certification requirements, and other requirements ensuring the safety and quality of the workers.
- Agencies can provide backup caregivers if your regular caregiver needs time off for whatever reasons.

- Most agencies maintain all required insurance coverages and handle any legal issues, including any theft or other complaints.

Home Care Agency CONS:

- Agencies need to mark up the hourly wages of their workers to make a profit, so you have to pay at least $5-10 dollars more per hour for caregivers you hire through these agencies. So, for example, you would pay $30 per hour for a caregiver who is actually only getting paid $20 per hour from the agency. The agency keeps the $10 per hour to cover overhead and other costs.
- Most agencies require a minimum number of hours for a shift, such as 4 or 6-hour minimum shifts.
- Agencies may also have other requirements, such as not asking the caregiver to do certain tasks such as deep cleaning and other restrictions.
- You don't have as much control and visibility into each caregiver's background, experience, and competence and are at the mercy of whoever the agency sends you. Of course, you can request a replacement caregiver for whatever reason, but that usually is only after spending a whole shift with one you don't care for much.

Directly hiring private caregiver PROS:

- You have complete control and visibility into the vetting and hiring process, the number of hours per shift, and job duties as mutually agreed between you and the private caregiver.

- You build a direct relationship with the caregiver rather than going through an agency, which can lead to better retention rates if you manage the relationship well.
- You can get a similar quality caregiver by finding them directly and offering to pay them more than they would get at an agency while still paying less than you would if going through an agency.

For example, you can hire someone for $20 per hour, which would be $5 an hour more than the caregiver would get at an agency. However, that would still be $5 less than the $25 per hour rate that an agency would charge you for the same/similar worker. At 40 hours per week, that $5 per hour savings would be an extra $200 in weekly savings.

Directly hiring private caregiver CONS:

- The burden of finding, vetting, and hiring a good caregiver completely falls on your shoulders. This can feel intimidating, especially if you've never done this before.
- You will also be in charge of background checks, tax withholding obligations, payroll, insurance, and other duties. This is probably the biggest pitfall of hiring caregivers directly, as the tax and insurance, related obligations, and potential liabilities for errors in this area can be quite significant.
- Coordinating care schedules may be challenging and time-consuming.
- Finding backup or last-minute replacement coverage can be very difficult and stressful.

∽

Tips on Directly Hiring Private Caregivers

If you decide to find and hire a private caregiver directly, there are several tips to maximize your chances for a successful experience. Here are a few things to keep in mind when finding and hiring paid caregivers:

Be specific on what or who you are looking for.

Be sure to list specific tasks and requirements in the job description, such as skills needed and experience and willingness to care for an older person.

Include as many relevant details as possible to avoid confusion or miscommunication about the position. For example, include the number of hours per week estimated, the detailed scope of duties, whether the position is for a live-in or live-out caregiver, the specific demands and needs of your loved one, and the pay range offered.

Here's a sample job description as a reference:

Our family is looking for a live-out capable, trustworthy, and punctual in-home caregiver to provide care for our elderly mother, who suffered a stroke and is limited to walking short distances assisted with a walker and otherwise spending time in her wheelchair and bed. We need someone with good communication skills, sound judgment, and who naturally looks out for the needs of others. Dependability, compassion, cheerfulness, and a positive outlook are necessary. A bright sense of humor will help you stand out as a candidate.

We require 8 to 12-hour daily shifts, 3-4 days per week. We may hire multiple caregivers to fill the remaining days of the week and appreciate candidates with flexible schedules.

Experience working with seniors is preferable.

Required skills:

- *Basic housework*
- *Meal preparation and simple cooking*
- *Comfortable bathing, dressing, toileting, and grooming elderly people*
- *Daily walks and exercise with the senior*
- *Organization*
- *Physical strength and stamina*
- *Time management*
- *Problem-solving*
- *Empathy*
- *Patience*

Benefits:

Change of schedule upon request

Some paid holidays off

Other requirements:

Willing to commute or relocate

Driver's License and clean driving record

Good references and clean background checks

<u>*Conduct an interview.*</u>

Request a resume and a list of references. Then, arrange an in-person interview with those who appear to be a good fit at your loved one's house or a local coffee shop. Or, if you prefer, you can do the initial interview by phone or video conference. Refer to the Appendix to see some *Sample Caregiver Interview Questions.*

The care recipient should attend the interview if possible because how they get along with the potential caregiver is important. You want there to be a nice and natural rapport there.

Do things the "legal" way.

You should make all payments above board. If you or your caregiver is subject to an IRS audit, the consequences could be significant if you pay them "under the table." It's not too complicated to create your W-2s and tax forms, but you can also utilize an accountant, an online payroll service such as Intuit, or a service tailored specifically for caregivers like Care.com's HomePay to assist you in getting the right forms completed.

Check references.

Even if the candidate you interviewed seems great, it's still a good practice to check their references and run background checks. Ask about the candidate's performance on the job, if they would hire them again, and whether they would recommend them for your position.

Also, do criminal background checks in all states where the person has resided or had employment because older adults are more vulnerable to being the victims of fraud or abuse.

Draw up a contract.

It is advisable to create a contract if you are hiring someone privately. The contract should be based on the job description.

Alternatively, speak with a lawyer to assist in drafting a straightforward agreement that outlines the basic terms of the arrangement (you can find some affordable contract attorneys on UpCounsel.com).

This would include the duties, hourly pay, paid vs. unpaid time off, the ability for either party to terminate the agreement with a certain amount of prior notice (for example, 2 weeks), and dispute resolution processes.

Retaining Paid Caregivers

Once you hire a great caregiver, how do you manage things to ensure a long and stable relationship?

What can you do to prevent turnover or unhappy workers?

Here are some tips:

Get to know each other well

Use your best efforts to get to know your parent's caregiver, as this will make them feel more valued, respected, and comfortable with you and your loved one. This aspect of familiarity allows you to form a stronger relationship. They will also be more comfortable coming to you with any concerns (and even better, with recommendations for improving your loved one's quality of life). You also develop lasting trust for the long term.

Maintain an open and honest line of communication. Encourage the caregiver to provide regular updates on how your loved one is doing. Your genuine attempts to get to know them better, the open communication, and showing your sincere appreciation and respect will yield a sense of loyalty from your caregiver that is priceless.

Be thoughtful and calm when handling problems and issues

There will be issues that arise even with the most experienced caregivers. Make sure you handle them tactfully, whether it's a minor problem (like your caregiver occasionally arriving late once in a blue moon) or a more challenging one (like a personality dispute with your aging loved one).

Ensure you handle each situation professionally and respectfully. For example, never insult or raise your voice with a caregiver and calmly discuss any issues and recommended solutions. Also, refrain from speaking with them when you're upset and give yourself some time to behave calmly.

You may find that a person you hire is a poor fit and needs to be let go. Make sure you evaluate the situation thoughtfully and objectively before making any hasty decisions. Ensure you line up a replacement caregiver quickly prior to dismissing your existing caregivers for continuity of care.

Check in with them regularly

Hiring a caregiver does not mean you can just walk away. While you may not do the actual day-to-day duties, you should still closely monitor how the care is being provided.

Ideally, check in with the caregiver at least once per week, either on the phone, Zoom or, even better, in person. Regularly checking in with them will give you a sense of how things are going and help you spot any issues before they become serious.

Make sure you also regularly privately speak with your aging loved one to get their perspective on how things are going with the caregiver. Your parent's care requirements will change over time, and you must pay attention to those changes as they take place.

By keeping closely in touch with the caregiver, you will be able to foster a positive long-term relationship with the caregiver for both you and your loved one.

. . .

<u>*Establish a secure environment.*</u>

It's your responsibility to provide the caregiver with a safe and healthy environment. When a family decides to hire a private caregiver, the senior may already be exhibiting hoarding tendencies or prone to violent outbursts, which are not uncommon side effects of dementia. Other diseases have side effects that may pose risks as well.

Make sure you are transparent and honest with the caregiver about any behavioral issues and let them decide for themselves if they feel fully equipped to handle such scenarios.

Establish healthy boundaries

Please note that private caregivers should not be required to take numerous calls outside work hours or stay late regularly. Remember that they have their own families and outside lives that need their time and attention. They also need to pursue other interests and activities.

In that regard, it may be possible that you need to intervene if your parent becomes overly dependent on or attached to them. It's best to keep your expectations reasonable and show respect if the caregiver warns you or your loved one when they go beyond the scope of their contract.

Ensure you exercise boundaries on your end as well. For example, if you and your siblings differ on how to care for your elderly loved one, don't ask or expect your caregiver to pick sides in any family disputes.

Also, exercise discretion when giving the caregiver substantial financial gifts or loans. These gifts might muddy the lines between personal and professional relationships, regardless of how close to the family they become.

. . .

Look for small ways to make working for your family more enjoyable

We all know how difficult and grinding caregiving can be. We also know how a little kindness can go a long way. Think of ways to brighten the moods of your caregivers by providing little perks here and there.

For instance, stock the kitchen with coffee, snacks, and other supplies, so they can access what they want while working. In addition, consider providing some reading materials to pass the time as your family member is sleeping or resting. Or let them know they can use the TV at certain times if all other tasks have been completed.

Also, remember their birthdays and give them little celebrations and gifts throughout the holidays to remind them how much you appreciate them. These little acts all make a huge impact on a long-lasting and healthy relationship. Ultimately, they are an extension of your family so try to treat them that way. And if ever in doubt, err on the side of generosity.

Arrange backup coverage care

Recognize that any caregiver will inevitably request time off, including in last-minute situations for emergencies and other urgent matters. Prepare for this contingency by having some home care agency retainers set up in advance so that you can use their services at a moment's notice.

This backup care option will alleviate your stress and any stress on your relationship with your regular caregiver. This ensures that you're never in a situation where your loved one is left without a caregiver.

Set clear expectations

It's best to make everything black and white regarding what you expect from your caregiver and vice versa. You want your caregiver to be well aware of everything your parent will require before they start working for you. You can create a list of all the things they frequently need assistance with and sit down with everyone involved in their care up to this point.

Be as specific as you can. For example, if you want cooking or doing laundry for your parent to be part of the job, please indicate that during the interview or include it in the job description. Don't assume that a caregiver will be able to accommodate all of your expectations; it's best to make everything clear from the beginning.

∿

Be Aware of Employment Laws

Please be aware that employment and other laws govern the working relationship between you and your privately-hired caregiver. This may include minimum wage laws, overtime rules, required breaks, and other wage and hour regulations.

In addition, every jurisdiction (state or city level) may have its own local rules, so check the regulations in your situation. For example, you can search for "caregiver wage and hour laws in [your state]" and see what comes up. By complying with such rules, you lower any chances of being subject to any dispute or lawsuit down the road.

While there are many specific legal issues in the field of caregiving and employment law, here are a few to be aware of:

Weekly salaries versus hourly rates. There may be wage and hour violations if an employer pays a caregiver a daily or monthly rate instead of a per-hour worked basis. Since caregivers are non-exempt workers, they must be paid for their hours, including any overtime. Review these rules in your state to ensure you don't run afoul of the applicable law.

Independent contractor misclassification. Most caregivers are classified as employees, not independent contractors. Many employers, however, still try to categorize caregivers as independent contractors to avoid providing them with the perks of being an employee, such as paying minimum wage and overtime.

Even if you have a signed independent contractor agreement with your caregiver, the law will invalidate any illegal independent contractor arrangement if the facts don't support a genuine independent contractor relationship. Just assume that your caregiver is a household employee and comply with all requirements associated with being an employer to a household employee.

Room and board deduction for live-in caregivers. Some employers insist that since they are paying for accommodation and board, they are exempt from paying minimum wage and overtime. That's not true. Only if the caregiver consents to such deductions in writing, and for a limited amount each month, can you deduct these expenses from their salary.

Sleep time deduction. This situation applies to those with 24-hour shifts. In general, sleep time should not be subtracted from hours worked in private homes. However, employers in facilities may take away sleep time under specific, extremely rare conditions. Be aware that caregivers could bring a claim against you if you deduct sleep time from their paycheck. Check the latest regulations on deducting sleep time for caregivers in your particular state.

∼

Recruiting Family Members to Help

Whether you hire paid caregivers or not, you may also want to recruit your siblings or other family members to help share the caregiving responsibility. Sibling caregivers frequently need to work together. While one sibling may live nearby and handle most of the daily caregiving duties, a long-distance sibling may offer remote-based help.

So, how can you involve your family members? You can use the family plan discussed in Chapter 2 as a starting point. To further flesh out the family plan and how to manage the relationships with your siblings or other family members, let's review some tips:

- Determine who will be responsible for each task during the meeting.
- Even if a primary caregiver is not immediately required, many families believe that naming one is a good idea. Then, in an emergency, the primary caregiver can take the lead and maintain clear communication.
- You must decide how your individual efforts will fit into the overall team.
- Ideally, each of you will be able to accept assignments most compatible with your hobbies or skill sets. For example, if someone is good at taking care of the finances, perhaps they can take over that task for your aging parent. If another is more skilled on the physical caring side of things, they can lead those efforts. It's also good to consider the limitations of each member and account for those in the family plan.

- Each family member should be realistic about what they can contribute and what they are willing to commit to.
- Consider how each member can modify their schedule to accommodate a primary caregiver's need for a break. For instance, family members can stagger their vacation plans so everyone can have some time off. Keep in mind that duties may need to be adjusted as circumstances, your care recipient's requirements, and the skills and limits of each family member change over time.

Addressing Difficult or Uncooperative Siblings

Now, it is possible that some of your siblings may not be able to or want to help. What then? Here are some tips on how to handle such challenging scenarios:

Don't expect that all tasks and responsibilities will be distributed equally. While the ideal situation is that care is equally distributed, the reality is that this is rarely the case. Rather than focusing on fairness, try to be practical and focus on how siblings can contribute in their own way, even if it's not as much as you would like them to.

Involve siblings who live far away. It makes sense that those nearby will be able to assist with picking up prescriptions, traveling to doctor appointments, or rushing to the emergency room in case of an emergency. Distant siblings, however, can still do their share by contributing monetarily or helping with tasks they can do remotely, such as doing research or paperwork.

Open communication. Maintaining open lines of communication with one another is essential to work effectively and preventing resentment. Don't expect a sibling to know when you need assistance, as they may not be as close to the situation and cannot read your mind.

Keep an open mind and maintain empathy for each other. It can be challenging, complicated, and emotionally taxing to negotiate with your siblings regarding parent care. Be aware of your emotions and empathize with your siblings' feelings, even if you disagree. Ask for what you need directly and specifically without feeling guilty or angry.

Acceptance of Unhelpful Siblings. It's possible that some family members will decline to assist with caring for your parents or will eventually stop. The best course of action might be for you to simply let it go if they aren't prepared to work toward fixing the issues. Attempting to change someone is unlikely and will make you feel more stressed and angry. If your siblings don't assist you, turn to friends, the community, or a professional for assistance.

Establish boundaries with toxic siblings. It's sad to say that some family connections are irreparable despite best efforts. Unfortunately, distance is sometimes the only practical solution in such a situation. Those with siblings who utilize coercion, guilt, and intimidation to get their way frequently find that distance is the best course of action. Although doing this can be challenging for various reasons, it is often the best course of action to eliminate unneeded stress.

No power struggles. If you have been given your parent's power of attorney over finances or health, please remember that it is your parent who has made these decisions. If your mother or father has given you power of attorney, keep thorough records and send your siblings letters detailing your spending of their parent's funds. While keeping records may seem like a lot of extra effort, it is required by law, and transparency will help avoid lawsuits and mistrust or distortion.

If it is the other way around (and your sibling was given a power of attorney), try not to take your parent's choice personally. To the best of your ability, provide current expenses and bills to the sibling with power of attorney. Bring in a specialist to explain your parent's needs and mediate if the sibling who controls the purse strings refuses to cooperate and reimburse you for your expenses.

Getting Paid as a Family Caregiver

Setting aside all these sibling issues, you may ask whether you can get paid for the caregiving service you provide to your loved one.

Government Programs

Unfortunately, very few programs compensate friends or family for providing care.

That said, certain Medicaid programs, such as In-Home Supportive Services (IHSS) and Home & Community Based Services (HCBS) waiver programs, may provide payment for family caregivers of qualified low-income seniors.

In addition, there are situations when families providing care may be granted financial relief for particular needs, such as respite care or buying products and services that Medicare benefits may cover. Refer to the Medicare and Medicaid sections in Chapter 3 for more details.

There may also be some grants or other forms of financial aid available to people with certain medical conditions from certain disease-specific organizations like CancerCare. These are rare, but it may be worth doing additional research based on your loved one's medical condition.

Direct Pay from your Care Recipient

If your parent agrees to pay you as their caregiver, it's important to have a contract in place with them for several reasons.

First, children frequently invest a significant amount of time and money in caring for an elderly relative, so it's appropriate for them to receive some form of payment.

Second, suppose there are multiple siblings, and one is more responsible for caring for the family's needs than the others. In that case, a contract can be useful to compensate the child for their efforts without unequally dividing the family's assets according to a trust or will.

However, the third and possibly most important reason to have a family caregiving contract is if your parent requires long-term care Medicaid, such as nursing home care, sometime in the future.

This is due to Medicaid's asset limit, which is $2000 in most states. Medicaid uses a 5-year (2.5 years in CA) "look back rule" to prevent seniors from gaming the system and "gifting" their assets to family and friends in order to reduce their assets to meet the $2000 Medicaid limit.

During this look-back timeframe, any assets that were transferred prior to your parent's Medicaid application will be carefully reviewed to make sure they were legitimate fair-value transactions and not just gifts. If Medicaid finds that any transfer was a gift, your parent will be penalized with Medicaid ineligibility based on the amount of such gift.

For example, if Mary's elderly mom has $35,000 saved in the bank, she would not qualify for Medicaid (because $35,000 is way over the $2,000 Medicaid asset limit). If her mom gives $33,000 to Mary and then applies for Medicaid within 5 years from the date of that $33,000 gift, then Medicaid would deny Mary's application for a period of time based on a formula they use. However, if her mom "spent down" that $33,000 by paying Mary as her caregiver (with a valid contract) over that same 5 year period, Medicaid would see that as a valid expenditure and not penalize her for that amount spent.

Medicaid ineligibility means that your family, not Medicaid, would need to shell out the money to pay for nursing home care (which is currently about $8,000 per month as a national average).

Therefore, you should have a family caregiver contract in place (signed and notarized) with detailed daily work/hour logs kept, in order to show that any payments that your parent made to you during any "look back period" were for legitimate caregiving expenses rather than mere gifts.

You should seek the assistance of an eldercare attorney to help prepare a personal care contract to ensure that Medicaid or other organizations will accept it. The contract should outline the services to be provided, your hourly pay (which should reflect the local market rate for paid caregivers), and the approximate number of hours per week that will be worked. Also, all payments should be paid after (not before) actual caregiving services were provided. See the Appendix for a *Sample Family Caregiver Agreement*.

∾

"Decide on Living Arrangements and Related Care Plan" Summary Checklist.

Reminders from this chapter:

1. Understand the various living arrangement options for your parent and decide if using a senior housing referral agency makes sense for your family.

2. If your parent is aging in place, determine your in-home care plan, including whether you'll hire paid caregivers, recruit siblings, become the primary caregiver yourself, or a combination of these.

3. Review the difference between home care vs. home health and which of the two your parent will need.

4. Determine whether you'll hire caregivers directly or through a caregiving agency.

5. Review the various considerations regarding caregiver hiring, compensation, retention, and employment law.

6. Review tips on how to recruit family members and deal with difficult siblings.

7. Understand the different ways that you can get paid as a family caregiver.

Selecting the right living arrangement and related care plan for your aging parent is fundamental to their long-term care plan. Equipped with adequate knowledge, you can help your family navigate these important decisions and feel confident that you're making the best choices for everyone involved.

6

LEARN THE CAREGIVING BASICS

Regardless of the various forms that caregiving takes, each family caregiver should have a basic understanding of how to approach the major practical aspects of day-to-day caregiving. This includes having a bigger picture of your aging parent's overall well-being, as well as knowing how to communicate effectively, handle memory issues, and how to use digital and other tools and equipment to make daily life easier for you and your loved one.

A Holistic View of Caregiving

Giving care involves more than simply meeting your loved one's urgent needs. A caregiver should think about the various aspects of their loved one's health, including their physical, mental, and emotional health. Let's examine what to look out for in each of these areas.

Physical Health

A big part of successful aging depends on physical health. Many of the most common and deadly health issues such as heart disease and diabetes are preventable by generally maintaining a healthy physical lifestyle such as healthy eating and leading a moderately active lifestyle.

Here are some suggestions to help your loved one maintain their physical health:

Eat real food. This may sound strange but it seems that a large portion of our diet these days involves some sort of processing and packaging. Replacing processed foods with more nutritious whole foods can drastically improve the quality of one's diet and health. An example would be substituting potato chips with a baked potato.

More veggies. Natural plants provide a sizable number of nutrients and fibers that provide the body with the fuel it needs to perform at its peak every day. Organic produce contains nutrients free from chemical pollution. In order to disguise the flavor of veggies for family members who dislike them, try blending them with sweet fruits like apples or berries. Many people who dislike veggies acquire their daily intake in this way.

Increase physical activity. Build a physical fitness and stretching routine for them. Aerobic exercise increases the blood flow toward working muscles and away from inactive muscles. The only way to strengthen our physical health is by exercise, which may be as easy as walking around the block or even some chair yoga at home.

Keep them hydrated. The general guidance is to drink at least eight glasses of water each day. The body is 60 percent water so replacing this water on a regular basis is important.

Keep a sleep routine for them. Observe your parent's sleeping patterns and encourage them to maintain a consistent sleep routine. Try playing a recorded guided meditation for sleep to promote relaxation and sleep. Have them refrain from using their phone or TV 30 minutes before bed. Plan their midday naps to enhance nighttime sleep. Create a peaceful, dark, and cool place with no clocks ticking or distracting lighting.

<u>Celebrate their humble successes.</u> Patience is the key to assisting someone in making healthy decisions. Encourage your loved one with praise when they eat a healthier option and when they've completed some exercise, and avoid pressuring them to make changes too quickly. Even the slightest progress is a win-so just start with small steps.

Know How the Body Ages

Every system in the body experiences changes as we age. Height recedes each year, and body mass shifts after age 70, with a 30% decline by age 80.

As caregivers, we will observe many of these bodily declines in our aging parents. As such, it is a good idea to become generally familiar with what changes are to be expected, and what are things to bring to the attention of your loved one's doctors.

Let's take a closer look at the various areas of physical change as one ages:

Eyes, Ears, and Mouth

- Fewer tears are generated
- Eye floaters (flashing lights and dots) increase
- Progressive vision loss: maintain frequent eye doctor visits to ensure proper prescriptions and glasses. Try getting bigger print books, a magnifying glass, large button phones, talking clocks, color-coded pill boxes, and adequate lighting for the home to help make things easier for low-vision seniors.
- Ear wax increases

- Progressive hearing loss: research technologies to
  amplify sound and improve common household goods
  for those with hearing loss. The local office of services
  for the deaf can offer specially designed phones,
  online signing services, and blinkers on phones and
  other devices to replace buzzers and alarms in most
  states.
- The senses of smell and taste decline with age, with
  taste buds losing their ability to distinguish the tastes
  of salty, sour, bitter, and sweet foods. This may lead to
  less enjoyment of food and related weight loss.

Muscles, Joints, and Bones

- Hand and leg strength declines
- Joints stiffen- combat stiffness by encouraging small
  daily movements and exercises. The less seniors move,
  the stiffer they become.
- Stride slows
- Muscles lose flexibility, strength, and endurance-
  leading to less coordination
- Bones shrink in density and size- making them easier
  to fracture and leading to height loss
- Balance while standing declines- leading to a higher
  risk of falls- refer to the *Home Safety Assessment* in the
  Master Caregiver Checklist in the Appendix to
  improve the safety of your parent's home.

Heart, Digestive, and Urinary Systems

- Blood vessels and arteries stiffen, causing the heart to
  work harder- increasing the risk of high blood
  pressure

- GI tract: waste product movement through the intestines slows leading to constipation. Constipation is made worse by a low-fiber diet and extended periods of inactivity. Encourage more water and fruit/vegetable consumption, think about supplementing the diet with dietary fiber, consider using a stool softener, or occasionally using a laxative (being careful not to create a dependence on laxatives). Also increase the senior's physical activity, as constipation is made worse by long periods of inactivity.

- Bladder becomes stiffer, leading to more frequent urination; weakened bladder muscles lead to urinary incontinence. Prescription drugs, minor surgery, or Kegel exercises are all forms of treatment for incontinence. Other interventions include creating a regular schedule for urinating, restricting fluid intake after supper, and wearing adult briefs. You may also want to consider using an external female catheter for an aging female loved one for nighttime use. More information can be found at purewickathome.com.

- Check with doctors if any medications may be causing or contributing to frequent urination/incontinence and make adjustments. You can also use waterproof mattresses, reusable or disposable protection pads, and nighttime adult diapers to address nighttime incontinence.

- Men can also use external condom catheters with a urine bag, but in my personal experience- the adult diapers were much easier to clean and deal with than the more complicated contraptions.

- Urinary Tract Infections (UTIs) are infections of the urinary system. Seniors with conditions such as incontinence, diabetes, kidney stones, or catheter usage can lead to more frequent UTIs. An untreated

UTI can lead to more severe infections or even sepsis, which can be life-threatening. You can help prevent UTIs by encouraging your loved one to drink plenty of water (as dehydration can lead to more UTIs), females should wipe from front to back when using the toilet, and take special care to ensure the cleanest possible environment when using urinary catheters. UTIs can cause sudden confusion (delirium) in seniors and those with dementia. If a loved one suddenly acts confused or agitated, it could be due to a UTI. Consult with your loved one's physician in such cases.

Cognitive Health

Seniors are particularly susceptible to cognitive and mental health difficulties due to memory challenges, cognitive decline, and a growing epidemic of loneliness.

Here are some suggestions on how to improve and maintain the cognitive and mental health of your aging parent:

Playing brain games

Brain exercises can improve short-term memory, planning abilities, reaction times, processing speeds, and other cognitive abilities. Any activity that keeps the brain active and striving to solve issues benefits brain health.

Some of the more popular and easily accessible brain games for seniors include crossword puzzles, riddles, and solitaire.

Finger Exercise Training

Also, try some finger exercise training games, such as asking your parent to touch their left thumb to their right index finger, then switch to touching their left index finger to their right thumb in a rhythmic, continuous motion.

These finger exercises improve fine motor skills and have been shown to increase cognitive health in elders- especially those who suffered strokes and other cognitive damage.

Reading and writing

Reading improves memory, lowers stress, and improves sleep. Journaling and writing help control and lessen the impacts of stress and anxiety.

Consider getting your loved one a simple adult coloring book and some colored pencils and see if they might enjoy coloring while listening to some of their favorite old songs. If limited vision is a concern, your loved one might also enjoy listening to an audiobook.

Playing an instrument

Seniors with Alzheimer's and dementia benefit from music's brain-stimulating effects and memory-improving effects. Playing an instrument, or learning to play one, can improve cognitive processing speeds within a short time period of several months.

Learning new skills

Teaching your parents how to use a cellphone or computer or how to use online services like YouTube and Netflix will entertain them and improve their brain health. While these may not strike you as new skills, they certainly are for aging people who are not familiar with using technology.

Picking up a new hobby

It's crucial to keep active in one's later years. When the brain is engaged repeatedly by visual stimulation, nerve cells can link or reconnect, changing the structure and function of the brain.

People experience comfort and a greater sense of belonging as neuronal connections in these pathways are reinforced and new connections are formed, ultimately boosting cognitive health.

After my dad passed away, I was concerned about the mental and cognitive health of my mom, who was very much in deep grief. I signed my mom up for some art and piano lessons to keep her busy. She was hesitant at first, but she ended up really enjoying the whole new world that learning piano opened.

She quit the art lessons so she could focus on the piano. I brought over an old electric keyboard for her to practice on and she has been learning piano diligently ever since. She really enjoys the interaction with her piano teacher every other Saturday and feels good about her progress and her goals. These piano lessons have been a true blessing for her (and me).

Maintaining Mental Health

Watch for signs of mental health disorders

A senior's overall well-being may suffer as a result of common mental health conditions including anxiety and depression. Mood disorders can cause impairments in physical, mental, and social functioning as well as have an impact on and make the management of other chronic disorders more challenging.

Depression and other disorders are not a normal part of aging, despite the fact that the prevalence of mental health conditions in older adults tends to rise with age.

Mental illness is a condition that can be managed clinically with the use of prescription drugs and therapy. Seek the support of mental health experts and support groups when diagnosing and treating possible mental health issues in your aging parent.

Encourage a Healthy Mindset

A positive outlook on aging will help your parents stay mentally, physically, and psychologically healthier. An optimistic outlook is expected to lower the risk of cardiovascular disease and cognitive decline and protect them from the typical stress and adverse experiences that come with aging.

Encourage your parent to read or listen to positive affirmations, teach them breathing exercises, and introduce them to guided meditations that can help them be calmer and more relaxed.

Also, be a good example by reminding them of the positive aspects of every situation and making it a habit to have an optimistic outlook in general.

Emotional, Social, and Spiritual Health

Although meaningful social interactions are necessary for all people, such connections are even more essential to maintain the quality of life of elderly individuals. Regular social interaction can keep seniors in good overall health.

Here are some suggestions on how to maintain your aging loved one's emotional, social, and spiritual health:

Help them stay connected with their friends

Maintaining social connections significantly reduces the negative impacts of aging. Talking to friends, exchanging stories, and engaging in conversations are similar to brain exercises like performing crossword puzzles.

See if you can organize some socializing opportunities such as bringing your loved one to church or the senior center to meet old friends or make new ones. You could also help your parent arrange a lunch outing with some of their friends or neighbors (or invite them over for a short visit if mobility is an issue).

Ask them to tell you stories

Ask your loved one to tell you stories from their past. Giving them the freedom and power of storytelling can raise their general sense of self-worth.

Reminiscing (or "reminiscence therapy" as defined by the American Psychological Association as the use of life histories to improve psychological well-being) can help people cope with negative emotions. It can also ignite areas of the brain that would otherwise be inactive, improving recall and memory in the process.

Watch your loved one light up when they recall a positive memory or funny story from the past. This can be a great way to pass the time, maintain a positive atmosphere, and improve your loved one's emotional and mental state. Consider creating a mini-documentary by recording your loved one telling their stories on your smartphone so you can share these with other family members for years to come.

Take them out and about

See if you can take your parent to participate in volunteer work in the community, sign them up for classes and activities, or go to the mall together. Take your parent out to eat, shop, watch a movie, or do similar things together at home or online if mobility is an issue. Celebrate birthdays and create other opportunities to let your parent get dressed up and have fun. These activities can raise their spirits and improve their overall health.

Play their favorite music and watch quality content

Your parent will feel better about life if they listen to their favorite songs, tap their toes to upbeat and pleasant music, and consume movies that make them laugh or are about stories of love, compassion, and inspiration.

Get them outside

Take a walk together, ideally in a natural or park setting, to enjoy the inspiring beauty of the outdoors and get a healthy dose of sun and fresh air.

The Magic of Human Touch

Give them enough human touch. Our wellness depends on touch because it soothes us and conveys someone else's concern. Oxytocin, the "feel good" hormone, is produced by your body whenever you make positive contact with someone. You also raise your dopamine and serotonin levels, aiding mood regulation and reducing anxiety.

Some advantages of this interaction include stress reduction, decreased anxiety and depression rates, reduced loneliness and isolation, increased trust, and encouragement of optimistic thinking. Seniors must get enough human touch because they are more vulnerable to isolation and related mental health issues. Regularly holding one's hand is a simple tip that can calm an agitated aging loved one and create an instant sense of connection between the two of you.

Deeper Dive on ADLs and IADLs

As a family caregiver, you should be aware of your loved one's capacity to care for themselves. As a part of this, you should know the difference between ADLs and IADLS. We already covered these briefly in Chapter 2, and you should be familiar with your loved one's care needs based on completing the *ADL and IADL Assessments* in the *Master Caregiver Checklist* in the Appendix.

That said, let's review the basics here again, as these will both be critical points to keep track of to determine how to best help your aging parent.

To review:

ADLs, or "activities of daily living," represent the most basic tasks that are essential to daily independent living such as feeding oneself and taking a shower.

IADLs, or instrumental activities of daily living, refer to more complex tasks that require more organizational skills that are also needed for everyday living, such as managing one's bank account and meal planning.

ADLs

Here are the main six ADLs:

1. Feeding: the ability to feed oneself.
2. Dressing: the ability to dress oneself.
3. Bathing/Showering: the ability to bathe, shower, and groom oneself.
4. Transferring: the ability to move oneself from one place to another.
5. Toileting: the ability to independently access, use, and leave the toilet.
6. Continence: the ability to control one's bowel and bladder movements.

A senior's ability to perform each ADL often serves as a gauge of their functional capacity and the level of care needed. These assessments are often used when determining the appropriate senior living arrangements such as assisted living or nursing homes, and to figure out how many caregiver hours will be needed to care for the aging loved one.

IADLs

Here are some examples of IADLs:

- Transportation: one's ability to handle their own transportation, whether it's through driving or accessing public transportation.
- Money Management: one's ability to handle their bank accounts, make on-time payments on their debts and look after their other financial assets.
- Housekeeping: one's ability to perform the independent chores required to keep a home tidy and prepare a meal, including grocery shopping and cooking.
- Communications: one's ability to maintain communication with others, such as telephone and postal correspondence.
- Medication Management: one's ability to obtain prescriptions and reliably take them as prescribed by a doctor.

You will likely need to help with some or all of these ADLs and IADLs depending on the level of care your aging parent will need as they age. Your level of involvement and your need to hire paid caregivers to help with these fundamental aspects of living will evolve over time.

～

Communicating Effectively with Aging Loved Ones

Engaging in Open and Productive Discussions

As your parent's caregiver, you need to have open discussions with your parent regarding their plans in several important areas. Common topics include making financial decisions, end-of-life planning, health care and senior living decisions, and certain other potentially challenging subjects.

You want to be supportive without becoming overbearing. Family members may be hesitant to bring up these difficult subjects and may keep them unaddressed, causing tension and pressure on the family.

Here are some suggestions to help initiate and carry on a productive conversation with your loved one:

Before beginning a conversation, be aware of your own feelings and emotional state. Assess if you're composed enough to conduct an effective conversation.

Take a few moments and consider what you want to accomplish through the discussion.

Make sure you set aside enough time for the discussion. Avoid rushing older people when speaking with them.

Keep the conversation brief to prevent draining your loved one. Divide lengthy discussions into shorter ones. Prioritize talking about the most critical subjects first.

Maintain a compassionate and gentle tone, especially when dealing with a depressed or anxious parent.

Give some general context of what you want to discuss and why it's necessary.

Speak clearly, calmly, and in a regular (not loud) tone, and minimize background noise. While speaking, maintain eye contact and face your parents. This will help them understand you better.

Empathize with your loved one by imagining yourself in their shoes.

Try to insert a few light moments and smiles into the discussion to maintain a relaxed atmosphere.

Choose your words carefully and stay away from frightening terminology. For instance, avoid using phrases like "cancer," "terminal," "irreversible," or "dementia" without precise diagnoses and use only when absolutely necessary.

Don't assume you're always right and have the best ideas. Keep an open mind and genuinely consider your parent's requests.

Arguing and correcting a parent with dementia is counterproductive. Recognize that a dementia patient's mind works differently than yours, and what sounds like nonsense to you may be a reality to them.

Make it a practice to ask questions instead of delivering advice when presenting discussion points and views. For instance, ask, "Have you had any trouble driving lately? " instead of "I think you need to quit driving."

Instead of forcing a resolution in one talk, split the discussion into smaller chunks.

Use this book to introduce your desired topic for discussion. For instance, you could say, "I've been reading this book on aging that has a lot of helpful advice." [State topic] was mentioned. Have you ever considered that?"

Introduce a topic by referring to a friend. For example, you can say, "My friend Martha said that her parents just finalized their estate planning docs and that it wasn't too bad." "Have you already prepared those documents?"

Prepare a notebook and pencil so you can take notes on conversations and takeaways.

Learning and applying effective communication methods can help you develop a more rewarding relationship with your aging loved one and move the needle forward on important decisions affecting their care.

~

Compassionately Addressing Resistance

Some parents refuse to acknowledge that they are having difficulties, despite it being clear to everyone else that they need help. By the time you notice changes or have safety concerns, you're likely correct: your parent requires some assistance. So, how should you become involved, especially if previous attempts to help out have been unsuccessful? Consider the following suggestions:

Be observant by looking for particular signals that an aging parent needs help or is in danger, including collecting information from others close to your parent. Seek feedback from friends, neighbors, and other family members to get a pulse on what is going on.

Listen carefully to your parent's perspective and concerns before attempting to persuade them to make a change. Try to understand and distill their needs and wants rather than convince them to agree with your opinions.

Determine the best course of action based on the facts and discussions. Create a general proposal to discuss with your parent and other family members. Depending on how resistant your parent is, discuss the best approach with the family to obtain your parent's buy-in. This may involve bringing in multiple family members or friends to reinforce the suggestion to your parent.

Get any necessary powers of attorney for financial and medical decisions. Review Chapter 2 for more details on these legal instruments that enable you to make decisions on behalf of your loved one. Once you have these documents, you can get your parent's agreement on which matters you (as their power of attorney) will handle on their behalf.

Brainstorm and assess your alternatives for the next steps. Consider the following: What appears to be the most urgent/important issue to address?

Decide and strategize. Based on your brainstorming, choose one to three areas to work on. If you have siblings or any other involved relatives, do this together and collaborate. Plan some clear action steps for each issue.

Execute your plan. It often requires multiple discussions and persistence to get things done, so be prepared for that.

By confirming that your parents need help, understanding their position, and addressing their concerns with the support of other friends and family members, your parent may become more open to accepting help.

By going through this process and remaining persistent, you'll be helping to get your parents more of what is necessary for their care and safety.

∼

Memory Care (Dementia and Alzheimer's)

What is Dementia?

Dementia is not a disease. Rather, the phrase refers to a wide spectrum of medical conditions produced by abnormal brain changes. Alzheimer's disease is the most common form of dementia, with the most common symptoms involving memory loss.

The prevalence of dementia increases as a person ages, with at least one in seven Americans over 70 having some form of dementia according to a study supported by the National Institutes of Health.

Because dementia impairs thinking skills, the patient's capacity to function independently in daily life suffers greatly.

While the subject of dementia merits volumes of research and books on its own, we will just cover the dementia basics so you know what to be aware of.

Dementia Warning Signs

- Loss of memory that interferes with daily activities
- Difficulty carrying out routine duties
- Language difficulties
- Loss of sense of place and time
- Poor judgment
- Difficulties with abstract thinking
- Misplacing things
- Mood and behavioral changes
- Personality changes
- Lack of initiative

Please keep in mind that not all symptoms are included, only the most prevalent ones. Speak with your doctor if you are worried about any of these symptoms. Diagnosing dementia is determined by a skilled healthcare professional following extensive evaluation and testing.

Dementia Treatments

Although there is no known treatment for the majority of dementias, there are ways to better manage and assist those suffering from it:

Medications

There are certain prescription medications that are used to temporarily improve dementia symptoms. Discuss with your parent's doctors to understand the pros and cons of trying these medications.

Some non-drug treatments include:

Occupational therapy. An occupational therapist can assist in making your loved one's home safer and teach coping skills. The goal is to avoid accidents, such as falls, help to control unwanted behaviors, and to help the loved one and the entire family be better prepared for the progressive nature of dementia symptoms.

Improve the environment. Reduced clutter and noise can help someone with dementia focus and work better. Knives and car keys, for example, may need to be hidden. Monitoring devices can notify you if the patient with dementia wanders.

Simplify chores and maintain routines. Break activities down into smaller steps and concentrate on successes rather than failures. Structure and clear routines also help in the reduction of confusion in those suffering from dementia. Consider writing out daily schedules and posting them on the walls to help remind your loved one of how to successfully go about their day.

Maintain general lifestyle adjustments. Dementia symptoms and behavioral issues usually worsen with time. Caregivers may want to consider the following general suggestions:

- Review how to communicate effectively with elderly people. Recognize that a dementia patient's sense of reality is different from a normal person's and it is often futile and unhelpful to repeatedly correct them.
- Encourage regular exercise and social engagements.
- Pay attention to mealtimes. As dementia sufferers sometimes forget to eat and drink, make sure they eat regularly and beware of choking hazards.
- Create a nighttime ritual. Dementia behavior is frequently worse after the sun goes down (aka "sundowning"). Establish relaxing bedtime rituals away from the sounds of television, meal cleanup, and energetic family members.
- Be generous with your genuine compliments and praise whenever they have a small success. Something as simple as, "I see your appetite is good today. That should give you a good boost in energy- great job Mom" can really lift their spirits.
- Just be with them. Some of the simplest, yet most loving and helpful things you can do for a loved one suffering from dementia is to hold their hand, listen to their stories, ask them how they're feeling, remind them of the positive things in their lives, be supportive and optimistic, and do what you can to help them maintain their dignity and self-respect.

∽

Getting Properly Equipped

Caring for an aging parent at home is difficult, but it can be much easier if you have the right equipment and tools.

Let's go through some of the basic equipment, items, and accessories for each major area of the home to ensure you have what you need to get the job done more efficiently.

Please research any additional tools or equipment that pertain to the specific medical conditions that your loved one may have by going to Google and searching for "[Name of Medical Condition] useful equipment and tools."

Bed

- Hospital bed (preferably adjustable in height and elevation to relieve the caregiver's back)
- Bed safety rails
- Bedside safety foam fall pads
- Mattress toppers and bolster pillows
- Over-bed table
- Waterproof mattress cover/pads
- Underpads for incontinence ("chux")

Shower/Bath

- Shower chair or tub transfer bench
- Handheld showerheads
- Adhesive non-slip stickers for shower or bath
- Safety grab bars
- Non-slip bath mats

Toilet

- Products for incontinence, including adult briefs (diapers), washable absorbent underwear, waterproof bed pads, and external catheters for men (condom catheters) or women (Purewick)
- Cleaning materials including wipes, rinse-free perineal wash, and rash ointment after cleaning
- Toilet safety rails
- Bidet attachments
- Toilet seat riser
- Safety grab bars near the toilet
- Bedside commode

Beyond

- Mobility devices such as a wheelchair, motorized scooter, Hoyer lift, entryway ramps, and stair chair lifts. Transport chairs are a good alternative to wheelchairs if your parent is unable to push themself. They are lighter and easier to take in and out of a vehicle. If there is no room for entryway ramps, an elevated platform lift may be another option to look into.
- Comfort/Orthopedic items such as grabber tools, heating pads, ice packs, chair cushions, and backrests. Inflatable chair cushions can help prevent pressure sores from sitting too long. Be especially careful of heating pads. Your elderly loved one may not be able to sense a potential burn.
- Equipment for the kitchen, such as electric kettles with auto-shutoff features, and electric can and jar openers to support those with weak hand muscles

- Devices for emergencies such as ID wristbands, medical alert necklaces or bracelets, smartphones preprogrammed with 911 and other emergency numbers, and wireless caregiver call button systems. One friend of mine keeps a clear zippered bag as a "to-go" bag. It includes her mother's id, insurance cards, healthcare power of attorney, advanced directives, medication list, health concern lists, tissues, water, snack crackers, adult briefs, gloves, wipes, and emergency medicine such as baby aspirin and nitroglycerin. It accompanies her mother whenever she leaves the house, including on a rescue squad or ambulance.

- Access to the home: keyless entry digital systems, keyless garage door openers, and video doorbells

Online tools

- For entertainment: Netflix, YouTube, Facebook, Tiktok, Amazon Echo speakers
- For communication: cellphones, Facebook Messenger, Zoom, FaceTime (this, of course, depends on your parent's willingness or ability to learn new technologies)

The use of the appropriate equipment and tools enables seniors to achieve a more relaxed, content, and independent existence. These tools also make it much easier for caregivers to help their care recipients. For a list of some of the tools I've found most helpful, please go to www.cynthiakaye.com and get the list of gadgets I recommend on the website.

Also, don't assume something is out of reach due to cost. Many programs may provide you with medically necessary equipment and accessories for little to no cost (Review Chapter 3 on Resources for more information on Medicare and Medicaid, as examples). Also, look around for local organizations that may provide free to low-cost rentals for equipment for seniors, such as walkers and wheelchairs.

∾

Quantity vs. Quality of Time Spent

When was the last time you actually sat down and looked your aging parent in the eyes?

Many aging parents feel like "they never see you" even though you feel like you're always there, rushing around the house like a mad person fixing things, prepping meals, and cleaning up—but they still don't feel like you're "there."

That can be frustrating as it feels like your parent is taking all of your efforts for granted and that they don't appreciate you.

However, that is not the case. What may be happening is that you're spending more "quantity" time than "quality" time.

While you feel like you're showing your love and concern by scrubbing their kitchen counters while your parent sits alone in the other room, they feel you're not even there. The result is that seniors lack the emotional support and connection they crave most.

What they may really want most from you is being next to them and actually "being" with them.

This may be very challenging for caregivers who haven't outsourced enough and haven't employed the right equipment and tools to make things more efficient. You may often think, "I don't have time to sit and chat. I have to get the dishes cleaned!"

The reality is that you can research the resources to give you more breathing room and outsource more so that you can spend those quality 20 minutes sitting down and having a cup of tea with your mom or dad.

Once you employ the right tools and outsource certain care-giving tasks, you will have freed up a significant amount of your time. You can spend this new-found time on any of your own priorities, including actually spending more quality time with your aging parent. This is what will matter the most when you reflect back on this special time together.

"Learn the Caregiving Basics" Summary Checklist

Taking a holistic view of wellness (body, mind, emotions, spirit) will meaningfully improve our caregiving experience. Focus on building knowledge, communicating frequently, and leveraging the right equipment and tools to work smarter, not harder.

Reminders from this chapter:

1. Consider all aspects of your loved one's physical, cognitive, mental, and emotional health.
2. Get more knowledgeable about ADLs and IADLs and how these assessments are used to find help for your aging parent.
3. Learn how to effectively communicate with your aging loved one.
4. Understand the basics of dementia and related care.
5. Know the appropriate equipment and tools to make caregiving more efficient.
6. Recognize the difference between Quantity vs. Quality when it comes to time spent with your loved one.

Regardless of the long-term care strategy you choose in the previous chapter, you must become familiar with the fundamentals of caregiving for your elderly parent. Getting a firm grasp of how to provide basic care, deal with resistance, ensure your parent's emotional and physical well-being, and use technology and tools to provide care more effectively will go a long way.

7

PRIORITIZE SELF-CARE

M any family caregivers find themselves juggling multiple responsibilities that compete and often conflict with each other. There are constant fire drills, persistent rushing from one place to another, eating on the go, and cutting into your sleep time to get things done. It seems nearly impossible to come up for air.

As we juggle our families, kids, aging parents, spouses, jobs, and other professional and social obligations, we hardly have any time to even think about taking care of ourselves.

This chronic lack of time and deprivation of attention to oneself catches up with caregivers and they are left exhausted, overwhelmed, and listless.

How can we address this downward spiral and perpetual merry-go-round of distress?

We've all heard the importance of caring for ourselves before we can truly take care of others. But the pressure to take care of oneself becomes yet another thing on our never-ending to-do list.

I know I feel that pressure. The pressure to eat better, sleep earlier, and get more exercise is another set of "to-do's" that is always chasing me.

Then I remember that it's ok not to hit all those goals and to give myself grace to just squeeze in what I can. Baby steps and celebrating small wins is a more sustainable approach.

While we should give ourselves grace, we still MUST prioritize our own well-being. While we may be able to sustain a relentless self-deprivation lifestyle for some time- maybe even a few years- eventually it will inevitably come crashing down and everyone, including you and your loved one, will suffer miserably if it gets to that point.

That said, let's look at the following areas of health and self-care that caregivers must attend to in order to maintain a baseline level of wellness.

Self-Care for Your Body, Mind, and Spirit

Maintain Your Physical Health

You can't be of much help if you're physically ailing yourself. Here are some pointers to help you maintain good physical health:

Maintain a balanced diet and sufficient hydration

Do your research on what the optimal healthy diet is for you. For many, an ideal healthy diet consists of mostly whole-food plant-based foods that are nutritionally balanced. Limiting processed, fried, sugary, and overly salty foods will prevent energy slumps and health disorders.

Sometimes, especially when we're exerting a lot of energy caring for someone, we get hungry between meals. Keep some nutrient-dense and wholesome snacks on hand. Fruit and nuts are convenient and healthy options.

Overeating can make you feel lethargic. There are easy strategies to reduce your portion sizes. Instead of using two slices of bread while making a sandwich for lunch, use one. Eat half of your breakfast in the morning and preserve the remainder for a mid-morning snack. Additionally, ask the server to box up half of your food for you to take home when you eat out.

Remember to hydrate. According to the National Council on Aging, adults older than 60 are at greater risk of dehydration which can lead to poor brain performance, digestive issues, and low energy.

Consider these tips:

Don't put off drinking until you're thirsty. You're already quite dehydrated by the time you start to feel thirsty.

Add flavor to your water if that encourages more drinking. Avoid sugary drinks with empty calories.

Get better quality sleep

Maintain a regular sleep schedule. Sleep deprivation is the worst thing you can do for your physical and emotional well-being. To get the most out of a good night's sleep, stay away from caffeine-containing beverages and electronic gadgets before bed and create a cool, quiet, and cozy environment.

Family caregivers must get enough sleep since they are particularly vulnerable to exhaustion. Caregivers frequently get up in the middle of the night to take care of their loved ones or finish their own responsibilities. Many family caregivers belong to the "sandwich generation" where they find themselves struggling to take care of their parents and their kids (not to mention holding down a job, cooking, and doing chores). While not everything is controllable, we can control when we sleep and stick with a routine to improve everyone's overall health.

Get regular physical movement and exercise

The loved one you care for may end up spending a lot of their time in bed, leading you to lead a sedentary lifestyle as a caregiver. However, it's important that you continue to move. According to the CDC, "being physically active can improve your brain health, help manage weight, reduce the risk of disease, strengthen bones and muscles, and improve your ability to do everyday activities."

Exercise is an optimal way to make time for self-care. Exercises to relieve stress are beneficial for caregivers since they boost the general mood and resilience while also enhancing physical health overall.

Consider working these 3 simple activities into your routine:

Aerobic Workouts. Increasing your body's endorphin levels as a result of some aerobic exercise is among the best ways to deal with stress. The pituitary gland and the central nervous system work together to produce endorphins. These substances, often referred to as neurotransmitters, help in preventing the transmission of pain impulses and, for some people, provide an overall sense of peace and even bliss. A bit of exercise can increase endorphin release naturally!

It doesn't have to be intense exercise. It can be as simple as stretching, basic cardio (walking or jogging), and some strength training (squats, lunges, wall push-ups, etc.).

In addition, you can build exercise into your everyday activities. Try pushing your loved one's wheelchair for a fifteen-minute walk around the block.

Yoga. While vigorous exercise is a terrific way to relieve stress and release endorphins, it should also be combined with scheduled downtime for rest and renewal. Yoga, an ancient Indian practice that combines breathing, concentration, and physical poses, can be a great way to get into shape from a mind-body perspective.

In order to bring the mind and body into harmony, restorative yoga focuses on calming and relaxing the breath and body. This kind of yoga allows those who experience a lot of stress to set aside time for themselves through slow, soft movements and prolonged silence. There are many short and sweet restorative yoga workouts on YouTube available for free and convenient sessions at home.

Outdoor time. Outdoor activities can include taking a light walk, forgoing the treadmill in favor of a neighborhood jog, riding a bike, or going on a simple hike. Household tasks like gardening, gutter cleaning, walking the dog, and raking can also be effective stress-relieving activities for caregivers who must remain near their homes. Take a book or magazine outside to read, take care of paperwork or work on the back porch or at the park, or attend to other tasks. Just get some fresh air!

Getting your tasks done outdoors or on the move not only naturally gives you some alone time, but also teaches your body to physically relax while performing daily duties. This method of multitasking is very helpful for caretakers whose schedules are jam-packed with numerous tasks and little time.

～

Mindset and Mental Health

It is far too common for busy caregivers to neglect their mindset and mental health. We mistakenly think that we can "save time" by neglecting ourselves. Taking care of our well-being must be nurtured to maintain your ability to function well and prevent burnout in the long run.

There's no good in saving a few minutes by skimping on our own needs today only to find ourselves completely unable to function tomorrow.

Here are some things to look out for to protect and preserve your mindset and mental health.

Organize away your stress

Review Chapter 2 on how to gather all the facts of your current situation and get clear on what your priorities and next steps are. Sometimes just the act of getting organized can make your problems seem much smaller and improve your mental state. When you know exactly what you need to do and have a plan for how to get things done, you have a sense of empowerment and confidence to move forward. Just take things one step at a time, keep learning, be super organized, and take advantage of the checklists provided in the Appendix.

Outsource, delegate, and accept help

Once you get organized and know what your prioritized tasks are, start brainstorming how to outsource as many of those tasks as possible. Anything that you can oversee, but don't necessarily have to actively handle day-to-day, are good candidates for outsourcing.

Review Chapter 3 on all potential resources that may be able to help you get the right information or funding, and consider using the family plan discussed in Chapters 2 and 5 to recruit your siblings and other family members to step up and relieve you of some tasks. Understand and use any respite and backup care options and think about when to hire paid caregivers for part-time or full-time shifts to relieve some of your shifts.

You should essentially be creating a caregiving "team" over time, resulting in your personal schedule freeing up. Delegating to these different members of your caregiving team, and maintaining a balanced schedule, can dramatically increase your mental state and quality of life.

Work on your Mindset

In Chapter 1, we talked about how critical it is to maintain a healthy mindset. It's literally the single most important element of becoming a great caregiver and maintaining your own sanity.

You are more than just a caregiver.

Your way of thinking determines how you live. Your attitudes and your beliefs directly impact your quality of life. Your stories and habits shape your reality, so what goes on in your head counts. Maintaining a self-care routine for your mind is as vital as taking care of your physical health.

What does this healthy mindset routine consist of?

Begin with self-awareness. Tune in to what goes on in your head. Remember in Chapter 1, we mentioned concentrating on things you can control. You can do that with self-awareness.

Your thoughts become more manageable when you tune in and become aware of them. You regain control because you can identify and replace unhelpful thoughts with a belief that is more useful. Mindfulness meditation and positive affirmations can help with this process.

Mindfulness is the practice of bringing your attention back to the present moment without judging it. It helps to train your mind to be calmer and clearer and is developed through practice. Positive affirmations are positive and encouraging statements that you repeat to overcome negative or self-sabotaging thoughts. We'll go over more on mindfulness and affirmations later in this chapter and Chapter 8.

Practice acceptance. Accepting a difficult circumstance does not imply that you agree with it. It simply means that you're not wasting time and effort regretting or overly lamenting the situation. When you give up resisting or catastrophizing a problematic situation, you have more energy to focus on finding solutions and optimizations. Remember there will be an end to this caregiving period and try not to see the situation as a burden but rather as an opportunity to help a loved one in great need.

Recognize the present moment. That is ultimately what mindfulness is all about. Our chronology is made up of a very little "now" that we are in. We spend our entire lives in that narrow window, but how much thought do we give to the present moment?

So frequently, we have our thoughts elsewhere, ruminating on the past or planning events that have not yet occurred. The only thing we can say for sure is that it is NOW. Make the decision today to pay attention and devote your whole focus to the moment you are in. Don't pass judgment on it. You only need to be completely awake and present while living in it.

Bookend your routine with gratitude. Active thankfulness is a practice that can improve your life. I know this one can be really hard when we feel exhausted and worn down. But, try hard on this one. It only takes five minutes a day to think about the things you are grateful for in your life instead of focusing on regrets.

No matter how bad things feel, there is always something to be thankful for. Can you walk? That's something to celebrate (as so many can't). Do you have all ten fingers? Thank goodness for that (as many don't). You get my point. These may seem trivial, but there really are so many who are in much worse situations. Recognizing this and being grateful for the little things we take for granted is good for our health. Consider choosing a journal to record three things you are grateful for every day.

Set and Maintain Boundaries

Caregiving can endure for years, and if you let it, can consume your life. Most of us didn't choose to be caregivers and didn't consider the challenges or time commitment required.

You need to be very open and candid when it comes to your limits and boundaries. The earlier you do this during your caregiving experience, the better.

How much of a commitment are you ready and willing to make? Get clear about what you can manage, what you'll do, and what you won't do.

Here are some tips to consider when determining your caregiving boundaries:

- Choose your "off" days or hours. Let people know that you won't be available during those times. Do whatever you need to do to recharge during that time.
- Rearrange your physical space for privacy. Configure the house and room set-up so that your loved one and

the rest of your family have some privacy and
separation. If your loved one is living with you, you can
consider building an addition to your house or use
room screens and separators to make some private
areas where you can spend some time alone.

- Practice saying "No." Caregiving can lead to physical
exhaustion and emotional stress, even in the most
loving and harmonious circumstances. Unfortunately,
caregiver burnout is unavoidable when you feel
entangled in a cycle of unreasonable requests and
believe you are unable to refuse.
- Saying no is hard in any situation. It can be much
harder when it's your aging parent who is making the
request or demand. But you need to establish
boundaries.

Setting boundaries with elderly parents is just as crucial as it
was for us to do with our children. As they get older, especially
if they have cognitive or memory loss issues, our parents might
not be aware of how demanding or unreasonable their requests
can be.

Elderly parents, who would normally be rational, make
unusual requests and flare up if their requests are denied. This
situation is especially true for those with issues like dementia.

One caregiving daughter exclaims, "She was never like this
before!"

"My dad has changed completely. He is so unpleasant and he is
making demands that are impossible," says another.

Learn to let go at a certain point. We have to understand and
overcome our feelings of guilt. Unfortunately, not all parents
are decent people, and not all of them looked after us well as

children and may continue to think they can behave poorly without consequences.

Naturally, we don't want to abandon them, but we don't have to subject ourselves to abuse either. Look to outsource, delegate, and manage from afar in these situations to protect your own well-being. It is not selfish- it is an act of self-preservation.

Making sure that our elderly parents are secure and shielded from danger as much as possible is the appropriate thing to do. Some parents reject assistance and appeal to enjoy a certain level of sorrow. We may not be able to change them. At some point, we have to let go and respect the boundaries we set for ourselves.

Calm the Overactive Mind

Meditation

Many of us suffer from "monkey minds," which is a term that describes a mind that jumps from thought to thought similar to how a monkey jumps from tree to tree. These monkey minds prevent us from ever taking a mental vacation from our constant internal chatter and negative recurring thoughts. Practicing mindfulness meditation techniques like the Loving Kindness meditation and some basic breathing exercises can help you relax and get a break from your relentless thoughts.

Here's an example of a Loving Kindness meditation you can repeat to yourself, allowing you to stay calm.

May I be safe

May I be healthy

May I be calm and peaceful

May I be strong

May I be thankful

May I show appreciation today and always

Repeat this as many times as necessary each day to bring you peace and calmness.

<u>Breathing Exercises</u>

It's amazing what a good, deep breath can do for your body and mind. For most, breathing comes as second nature and most people don't pay much attention to it. But focusing on your breathing with some exercises can do wonders for improving your state of mind. Here are a few to try:

Exhaling longer. Sometimes deep breathing won't help you relax. The sympathetic nervous system, which regulates the fight-or-flight response, is actually connected to deep breathing. However, the parasympathetic nervous system, which affects our body's capacity to relax and calm down, is connected to exhaling.

Try a full exhale before you take a huge, deep breath. Let your lungs accomplish their job of breathing in air by forcing all the air out of them.

Next, attempt to exhale a little bit more slowly than you inhale. Try breathing in for four seconds and out for six, for instance.

For two to five minutes, try to practice this.

You can use this technique while standing, sitting, or lying down, depending on which position is most comfortable for you.

Belly breathing. To do this, please lay down or sit. Put one hand on your chest and the other somewhere over your belly button on your stomach.

As you inhale deeply through your nose, you'll feel your tummy rise. Your chest ought to be mostly motionless.

Lips pursed, you may exhale through your mouth. As you exhale, try contracting your stomach muscles to force air out.

Try practicing this type of breathing every day for it to become automatic. Try performing the exercise for up to 10 minutes, three or four times a day.

Alternate nostril breathing. Please sit down in a comfortable position, stretch your spine, and open your chest to practice alternate nostril breathing.

Raise your right hand while keeping your left hand on your lap. Next, place your right hand's pointer and middle fingers on your forehead, in the space between your brows. As you breathe in and out through your nose, close your eyes.

Close the right nostril with your right thumb and exhale fully and slowly through your left nostril.

Once you've completely exhaled, release your right nostril and close your left nostril with your ring finger.

Breathe in slowly and deeply with your right nostril. Hold your breath for a couple of moments at the top. Then exhale completely from the same right nostril.

Release your left nostril and close your right nostril with your thumb once again. Take a deep inhale, hold for a few moments, and then fully exhale from your left nostril.

Repeat this up to ten times, and breathe in and out through one nostril at a time. Studies have shown this technique to calm the body and mind and relieve stress.

Emotional and Spiritual Health

To maintain emotional health, you need to fight isolation, anxiety, and depression. Caregivers frequently try to do everything on their own and begin to put relationships with their friends and peers on the back burner.

To sustain emotional wellness, social interaction is essential. Join support groups (both offline and online), and don't forget to speak to friends on the phone or in person. People are less likely to experience depression and anxiety when they feel connected.

Signs of Depression

It's best that you watch out for signs of depression and seek professional help without delay if needed.

Here are some signs of depression to look out for:

You are consistently in a bad or low mood. As human beings, we all experience bad moods but prolonged periods may be an indication of depression if it lasts longer than six to eight weeks. Depression can be accompanied by an overwhelming feeling that everything is closing in on you.

You are disinterested in activities you previously enjoyed. Your favorite pastimes and experiences play a significant role in who you are. When you stop enjoying the things that used to make you happy, it may be a warning of something more serious to look into with a professional.

Concentration and memory issues. Because of how depression affects the brain, many depressed individuals also have memory loss or difficulties concentrating. This might be a result of depression's impact on the brain's tendency to dwell excessively on negative memories and thoughts.

Significant changes in eating or sleeping habits. Depression frequently causes changes in appetite. Many people either use food to elevate serotonin levels or repress feelings. Others occasionally have a complete distaste for food or lack the energy to prepare and eat a meal.

Similar to how inadequate or excessive sleep can be a sign of depression. Extreme exhaustion brought on by increased intrusive emotions can result in oversleeping, whereas hyperarousal and stress can disrupt sleep patterns and result in undersleeping.

Positive Affirmations

Affirmations are positive statements repeated (either out loud or silently) by people to increase self-confidence and positive beliefs in themselves. Many have practiced positive affirmations without realizing it, such as when they tell themselves "I got this" before a job interview. Unfortunately, many also practice negative self-talk without realizing it when they say harmful things like "I'm so stupid" or "Life sucks."

Our brains often can't distinguish between reality and imagination. That's why imagining a situation (such as winning a race) activates many of the same regions of the brain as experiencing the real thing.

Therefore, telling your brain positive statements encourages your brain to believe these as real. These beliefs within your subconscious mind then manifest into actions that are aligned with those positive beliefs. It becomes a positive self-fulfilling cycle.

You can consume positive affirmations by reading them, speaking them aloud, or by listening to them in an audio format. This helps fill your subconscious mind and spirit with uplifting and empowering beliefs.

Here are a few positive affirmations to build into your daily routine:

I am valuable and my work is important.

I am a kind and capable caregiver.

Taking care of my aging parent is a blessing.

I deserve laughter and love in my life.

My compassion and love are powerful.

Self-Care when Dealing with Grief

Anticipatory Grief

Caring for a loved one who is seriously ill or generally declining with old age comes with its unique type of grief. With most chronic conditions, we watch our loved ones decline over time. As we see their increasing loss of abilities, we anticipate and fear the additional losses they will suffer. We also know that their end is likely near. The anxiety and sadness this creates are referred to as anticipatory grief.

Anticipating the loss of your loved one's abilities and mourning the losses they've already suffered can be just as painful as the loss experienced after the death of a loved one. The loss associated with witnessing the continual decline of a loved one and the fear of their impending death can be extremely stressful and cause a great deal of anxiety.

It's important to acknowledge that anticipatory grief is very common among caregivers. Anticipating sorrow may actually be our mind's way to help us become more emotionally prepared for the inevitable loss of our loved one.

But don't feel like you need to stay in this state of anticipatory grief all the time. If you can manage, do the self-care exercises in this chapter and in Chapter 8 to encourage your spirit despite the difficult circumstances.

Making end-of-life plans, including arrangements for the funeral and burial, can help family members reflect on and address outstanding issues, as well as experience their pain gradually. When someone has been grieving a death for a while, there may sometimes be less grief when the person passes away. Everyone deals with loss in unique ways. You may consider journaling and practicing mindfulness techniques to reflect on your emotions during your grieving periods.

Grief after death

Then there's grief when caregiving ends. Caregivers sacrifice much of their own lives to take care of others. Much of their identities and daily routines may revolve around their caregiving roles. All of this comes to a screeching halt once the loved one passes away.

Caregivers will need to decide what to do with their lives and their remaining identity once their care recipient is gone. There is often little or no planning for this change. In most cases, you were so busy providing care that you didn't have the time, energy, or mental fortitude to consider what would come next.

The following suggestions may be helpful:

Recognize your feelings of loss and relief are normal. It is very common among caregivers to experience both a deep sense of loss, grief, and sadness as well as a deep sense of relief when their loved one passes away.

You should not feel guilty about the sense of relief you feel. You have undergone a very difficult period of sacrificing many things in order to do your best to help your loved one. You are probably quite exhausted, both physically and emotionally, from everything that led up to your loved one's passing.

It is only normal to breathe a deep sigh of relief- relief that your loved one is no longer suffering, and relief that you can also get some deeply-needed time to recharge yourself.

It's common for the grieving process to take a year or more before you feel "normal." But some recover much more quickly. I was so terrified before my dad passed that I was going to be a total emotional wreck for years. I was afraid that I was going to fall into a bottomless pit of grief. My dad really was one of my closest confidants and best friends, so the thought of losing him terrified me.

To my surprise, I did not fall into a bottomless pit. I was actually able to function quite normally. Of course, I felt deep grief and sadness and cried a lot (and I still do spontaneously cry when something triggers a memory of him), but I felt a deep (almost magical, actually) sense of peace and calm immediately upon his passing.

I think a big part of that peace was that I knew, deep down inside, that I really did my best in taking care of him during his last moments.

Don't get me wrong: I made tons of mistakes as his caregiver. And there are many things about my behavior and impatience with him that I still feel horrible about (even though I know I shouldn't).

But that did not take away the sense of peace I had (and continue to have) once he was gone. I'm very grateful for this sense of peace that I did my best for him (while keeping my own boundaries).

Everyone processes grief on different timelines and there is no right or wrong way to do it. It can help to speak openly about your feelings of grief with friends and family members and try not to suppress, hide, or rush those feelings. When I feel grief welling up inside my chest, I brace myself and let the feeling express itself fully within me. I feel the pain of loss and I just let myself fully feel it. I usually cry. And then it passes after a few moments and I'm able to move on with my day.

Forgive yourself. Self-forgiveness is important because caregivers frequently feel guilty when reflecting on the shortcomings they exhibited as a caregiver. Every caregiver has experienced moments of impatience, rage, frustration, and even cruelty. You probably couldn't have done anything otherwise in that moment, despite your belief that you could have.

It's OK.

Stop bringing up "what if" situations. Stop beating yourself up over that terrible thing you may have said in a fit of rage. We have all been there and it does not make you a bad person. Caregiving can be a relentless job that can push people to the brink of insanity.

You did your best under the circumstances and you were there as much as you could be. Rather than feeling guilt, be proud of the commitment, love, and care that you did provide.

Rest and sleep - you deserve it. Exhaustion is frequently one of the first reactions that caregivers experience after the death of their loved one. The hour has come to go to bed. You must replenish your energy. Sometimes you simply need to curl up under the covers and watch TV or remain in bed and cry. You're entitled to a good long rest.

Request bereavement leave if your employer provides it. You may find that solitude and quiet time is just what your soul needs to recover and move forward.

Rebuilding Your Life When Caregiving Ends

What happens when your role comes to an end? What can you expect when this time comes?

It's time to rebuild your life.

After giving someone else so much of your time and commitment, it can be difficult to put your own needs and grief management first. It's time to redirect your attention from your loved one and put it toward reviving your own emotional, spiritual, social, and physical well-being.

Emotional Recovery

The obligations of caregiving sometimes become too overwhelming. Naturally, being overwhelmed for so long has a negative impact on one's emotional well-being. Your task now is to find emotional and spiritual healing.

During this period of self-discovery and grieving for your loved one, there are helpful techniques that may assist in your recovery:

Perform rituals. There is no requirement that rituals be witnessed by others. Rituals can be any straightforward activity that helps you relax and reflect on the dearly-held memories of your loved one. If it provides you calm, embrace it and return to it as often as you need during your grieving and journey of self-discovery.

Examples include journaling, lighting a candle and praying, playing your favorite songs or those of your loved one, or something as mundane-seeming as washing your car or folding your socks, while reflecting on how far you have come through all of this.

Take a break from all the sadness and grief. Taking breaks from your sadness is allowed and will help you rebuild your life. We are greatly diminished by grief. Constant sorrow exertion is similar to heavy physical exercise. It is OK to take a break from the strain of grieving. Allow yourself to do things that bring you enjoyment, such as going fishing, watching a funny movie with family or friends, or simply taking a walk in the park. There should be no guilt in smiling and laughing while you are still in your grieving period.

Seek professional help. Each person's grief is distinct, and sometimes the road to recovery and accepting a new life can be a difficult one. You don't have to go through this period of loss and grieving alone. You can seek support from a qualified professional therapist.

Asking for help is never a sign of weakness. You can get a wealth of knowledge and awareness of what you need during this time and how you will most effectively find your road toward healing throughout the grieving journey by utilizing the expert perspective and coping mechanisms provided by a professional.

Social Recovery

We need positive connections with other people, even though we may not always feel like it, especially after going through a traumatic loss and significant life upheaval. Reconnecting and developing supportive relationships with others can be extremely helpful during the grieving and healing process, especially with others who have gone through similar experiences.

How do you begin?

1. Reach out. It's not necessary for everything to happen at once while you work to rebuild your social life. Laying the groundwork for reconnecting with others might start with taking modest measures, such as a quick coffee meet-up with a friend or a quick phone conversation with a family member.

2. Re-establish ties with your church or another place of worship or neighborhood initiatives. Many caregivers stop participating in activities that require leaving the house because of the obligations of providing care. After the caregiving phase of your life is over, gradually become re-engaged in the organizations and causes you formerly supported. Restoring healthy social connections can be greatly facilitated by brief interactions with neighbors and simply leaving the house for a while.

3. Join or organize a support group of loved ones, friends, and other caregivers. When going through the mourning process, talking to trusted people who genuinely care about your well-being is a powerfully uplifting influence. One of the most crucial tools you may use is your family's support. The mere fact that

you can talk to and rely on people you love can give you that sense of comfort and security you need.

Physical Recovery

Physical care is an essential part of reclaiming one's identity after stepping down from the caregiving role. Rebuilding your identity and reviving your entire being requires refocusing on your physical well-being.

Here are some tips to rebuild your physical fitness:

Exercise. Regular physical activity has been shown to reduce stress, release "happy" hormones, and enhance one's view of life. You can begin to invest in your physical well-being by just going for a 15-minute walk whenever it is most convenient for you. There is an old proverb that says "A journey of a thousand miles begins with a single step."

Rest. You did not get enough of this when you were a committed caregiver. Restorative sleep was all but impossible because of worries about what would happen the next day, doubts about whether you had done enough for your loved one, and the overall, constant stress of caregiving. Catch up on sleep now whenever you get the chance.

Meditate. By practicing meditation, you can quiet your mind and free it from the constant chatter of worries, tensions, and ideas. Spending just five minutes of your morning routine in meditation can help you start the day in a calm and alert frame of mind. There are plenty of free meditation videos on YouTube or you can also try some meditation apps on your smartphone such as Insight Timer, Headspace, or Calm.

⌇

"Prioritize Self-Care" Summary Checklist

Reminders from this chapter:

1. Address and tend to your self-care pillars of maintaining your physical, mental, and emotional health.
2. Practice self-care when dealing with grief and with any of life's challenges in general.
3. Re-establish your life when your caregiving journey ends.

Burnout can result from the exhausting physical, mental, and emotional responsibilities of caring for an aging loved one. Maintaining your own health and well-being is fundamental to giving the best care to your loved ones.

Once the caregiving comes to an end, seek healing and start to live a life sparked by a new purpose.

8

BONUS SECTION: CAREGIVER BURNOUT AND HOW TO ADDRESS IT

The dangers of caregiver burnout for both the caregiver and the care recipient are significant and preventable. Let's dive into what caregiver burnout is, what causes it, and how to prevent or recover from it.

What Exactly is Caregiver Burnout?

Some people refer to caregiver burnout as "emotional weariness," where they feel an increasing emotional distance from the duty of caregiving. This may be an act of self-preservation to help the worn-out caregiver maintain their own sense of balance, which has been worn out by the overwhelming demands of caregiving.

Burnout can cause caregivers to grow distant from their care recipients and even resent them. Burnout is the stage at which caregivers are frequently unable to continue in their caring tasks and care recipients are most at risk of institutionalization.

When you try to do more than you are capable of, either physically or financially, or when you don't have the support you need, the result is often burnout. Fatigue, worry, anxiety, and melancholy are common in caregivers who are "burnt out."

In addition, a lot of caregivers feel guilty if they choose to take care of themselves rather than their sick or aging loved ones. This exacerbates the problem and perpetuates the burnout.

Symptoms

It's important to understand the warning signs of caregiver burnout so you can act quickly to stop things from getting worse. Burnout in a caregiver has symptoms that are comparable to those of severe stress and depression. They include:

- Lack of interest in past interests
- Frequently irritable and angry
- Emotional and physical exhaustion
- A deeper and more prolonged sense of hopelessness
- Frequent illness
- Neglecting responsibilities or harsh attitudes toward the care recipient
- Wanting to harm yourself or your care recipient
- A sense of incompetence when providing care
- Loneliness or social isolation
- Heightened anxiety and depression
- Overreacting to minor problems
- Having difficulty concentrating
- Consuming more alcohol, smoking, or food
- Appetite and sleep patterns change
- No longer caring what happens to you or your care recipient (just giving up)
- Disregarding your personal needs, both physical and emotional

Additional factors that can contribute to caregiver burnout include:

Overburdened with too much responsibility. Juggling between caring for an elderly parent and your own children is typical for those in the "sandwich generation." Without the right systems in place, juggling these competing priorities while trying to keep a full-time or part-time job can push people past their breaking point.

Excessive emotional weight. Some caregivers carry too much emotional weight, whether they obsess about how they got pulled into the caregiving role or guilt over how they should have done more to prevent their parent's decline earlier. There also may be excessive resentment and constant feelings of wanting the situation to be over.

There's also often regret about being overly irritable or harsh with the aging parent. There is even more guilt about not spending more time or not doing a good enough job as a caregiver. These heavy emotions accumulate and eventually crush the caregiver's spirit.

Lack of privacy or any alone time. Caregivers who spend most of their waking hours next to their aging loved ones find that there is no space or time in their schedule to be alone. This constant lack of privacy wears down their psyche, and they increasingly feel anxious and trapped.

Consistent poor nutrition and lack of sound sleep. Aging loved ones often need help throughout the day and night. Without a firm routine, many caregivers are left with shoving fast food or other unhealthy foods in their bodies and often have interrupted and unsound sleep.

Confusion about your role as a caregiver. It can be difficult to distinguish between your roles as their child, caregiver, or their friend.

Savior complex. You may want to fix people's problems and increasingly feel frustrated and hopeless when you can't prevent the steady decline of your aging parent's health. This is particularly hard for those whose loved ones are suffering from a progressive and incurable condition like Parkinson's or Alzheimer's.

Lack of social connections. With such a busy schedule and wanting to take care of your loved one all the time, you gradually stop engaging with anyone else outside your care recipient. Your world starts feeling very isolated and shrunken as if the rest of the world has left you behind.

Lack of control. Your frustrations become exacerbated by your constant lack of funds and stress about obtaining sufficient funds to manage your loved one's care. You respond by doing more and putting in more hours of your own time, leading to even more exhaustion and burnout.

Lack of appreciation and lack of support from others. Your loved one's diminished physical and mental state makes them unappreciative and demanding patients who never thank you and always criticize you. Despite knowing they don't realize the unfairness of their actions, this constant barrage of criticism and lack of gratitude triggers feelings of rage and resentment inside you.

How to prevent burnout

Leaving caregiver burnout unattended and left to fester is a recipe for disaster for you and your loved one. The very act of trying to help your loved one has turned into a disastrous situation where you may actually pose a danger to yourself and your loved one. You must seek help and take prompt steps to reverse your burnout.

When possible, follow these suggestions BEFORE your burnout becomes incapacitating. Recognize that caregiver burnout occurs on a spectrum, typically beginning with general exhaustion, progressing to despondency, and culminating with full burnout, at which point the caregiver becomes numb to everything. The earlier you can implement the self-care advice here and in Chapter 7, the higher your chances of avoiding this debilitating condition.

There are a number of helpful techniques to ward off burnout and stress. It's crucial to have a variety of stress management methods at your disposal. Then, you'll be able to select the approach that best suits your current situation.

Join caregiver support groups. Look for caregiver support groups on Facebook and other online sites. Ask your hospice provider if they know of any nearby caregiver support groups if your loved one is receiving hospice care. Listening to others who are in similar situations lets you release your pent-up emotions.

Maintain at least a few key relationships. Even if you're feeling swamped or anti-social, do your best to maintain your connections with at least one or two close friends or family members. This could be just a five-minute phone call once a week to say hello. You can either vent about your frustrations, or you can talk about something else entirely. One note: make sure to avoid negative people who suck your energy and lower your outlook and mood.

Keep a journal of your feelings. You don't need to devote much time- just a few minutes a day can be a helpful outlet. You can handwrite a journal entry, or you can also just type yourself an email if typing is easier and more efficient. Just have a way to express your thoughts, and don't judge what you're writing- just write. Nobody ever has to see anything you've written.

Set realistic goals. Set these goals for your ability to give care and outsource or delegate the rest. Accept that some things will need to be handled by others.

Prioritize. Decide which are the most vital chores and be willing to delay the less important ones.

Be direct. Be more outspoken and direct when asking siblings and other family members for assistance, and accept help when it is offered.

Use Respite Services. Utilize the services of your hospice provider or local assisted living facilities for respite services.

Consume media selectively. When you have free time, consume positive, humorous, uplifting movies, podcasts, or books. Audiobooks can be efficient to listen to while commuting or folding laundry.

Consider if your loved one should move. Recognize your limitations and exercise objectivity when determining whether or not your loved one would benefit more from living in an assisted living or skilled nursing facility.

Don't baby them. Don't overprotect your parents by doing things for them that they are still capable of doing on their own.

Don't take things personally. Recognize that it is the disease or condition that is affecting you and your parents. Both of you are fighting the illness together, not against each other. Don't take the changes in your parent's behavior personally.

Allow yourself to take breaks. Get out of the house. Take a bubble bath. Treat yourself to the small and simple luxuries by telling yourself that you are worth it.

Maintain your own wellness. Do not cancel a visit to the doctor because you are too busy. Keep up with your own medical, dental, and vision checkups.

Pace yourself and maintain flexibility. You must balance your energy and time while juggling your caregiving responsibilities with your needs. Additionally, you should keep an open mind because change is the only constant in the life of a family caregiver.

Consider taking time off work. Find out more about Family and Medical Leave Act (FMLA), which allocates up to 12 weeks of unpaid leave per year for family caregivers, by contacting your HR department.

Let go of what you can't control. Do not evaluate your success based on your loved one's state of health. The truth is that aging cannot be stopped. Serious chronic illnesses will keep getting worse. At some point, we must let go and accept the situation as a part of life.

Do not look to your aging parent for approval. Or praise, or appreciation, for that matter. Being underappreciated for all the work you put into caring for your elderly loved one is very common. Remember, their diminishing cognitive state limits their ability to understand the situation and recognize all the work you're doing for them. Don't take it personally.

Continue your exercise regimen. It can make a significant impact to take even a little 5-minute break to stretch and perform some lunges and squats. Or, even better, spend 10 minutes obtaining fresh air by walking around the neighborhood.

Eliminate stress-causing activities. Occasionally, giving up something in your life is the best way to relieve stress. Remove the stress-inducing items from your life so you can live a more peaceful life. Just a few things cut out or reduce watching the news, being constantly plugged into your electronic devices, consuming alcohol, and taking in too much coffee.

Try meditations or affirmations. Start meditating for 5 minutes a day and see how you feel. Your goal is simply to relax, breathe, and be present. There are a lot of guided meditation videos online, like YouTube, where gentle, loving, and compassionate people guide you to practice mindfulness to find peace and joy. Try searching for "10-minute guided meditations for peace" on Google or YouTube to get started.

Both immediate stress reduction and long-term advantages for stress management come through meditation. There are many different meditation techniques to try; each one is distinctive and appealing in its own way.

As I shared earlier, repeating affirmations can help you feel more motivated and optimistic. Powerful words can activate new areas of your subconscious mind.

Try these affirmations any time you feel negativity or burnout:

- I am doing my best and proud of myself.
- I can handle anything that I put my mind to.
- There are many things to be thankful for.
- I am resilient and strong.
- I love myself and my family.
- I am worthy of taking breaks and enjoying life.
- I am making an important difference.
- I am my parent's best caregiver.

You won't be able to dwell on the past or worry about the future when your attention is on the present. Although they take practice, mindfulness and meditation can significantly reduce your overall stress by bringing you back to the present.

How to Reverse Caregiver Burnout

If your burnout state is already severe, you may require more urgent action to address it. If you've already come to the point where you are utterly numb to your caregiving responsibilities, you must seek help as soon as possible.

Find temporary replacement care

First, do everything you can to set up replacement or respite care. Call a close friend or family member to let them know that you are not feeling well and may need to go to the hospital. This way, your friend or family member will realize the severity of your condition.

You don't need to explain any details to this friend or family member. The point is to get relief and make sure your loved one is safe while you seek further assistance. You can address prying questions with "I'm feeling quite ill and can't talk much about it now. I appreciate you relieving me for a short while, and we can connect as soon as I get a bit better. Here is where you can reach me in a true emergency."

Another route to find respite care is to ask a friend to help you set up a Go Fund Me account to raise some donations and funds to pay for a few weeks of paid caregiver assistance so you can take that time off entirely.

. . .

Use the time off to get therapy and recover

Take advantage of the time off to seek professional assistance, get some rest and sleep, and work on some of the self-care recommendations in this chapter and Chapter 7. Before you can resume your caring responsibilities, you must focus on regaining your physical, mental, and emotional health. And remember to be gentle with yourself as you heal.

Returning to caregiving at a sustainable level

During your time off, determine if you can return to your caregiving duties. If possible, review the steps in this book to revisit any untapped resources, get more organized, and see how you can re-configure your caregiving team to relieve yourself of as many tasks as practical. Outsource as much as possible so you can prevent a burnout relapse.

Finding the best techniques to ward off your burnout, in the long run, will likely take some trial and error. Since caregiving can be a very long-term journey, recognizing your symptoms of burnout each time it creeps up, and having the skill set to address and nip it in the bud, will enable you to stay healthy and able to continue to care for yourself and your loved one without regrets.

≈

Caregiving is a Balance

Remember that caring for your aging loved one is ultimately a balancing act. You have made a very noble and compassionate choice to help your loved one. But you need to balance your caregiving duties and your own needs in order to have a sustainable situation.

As family caregivers, this balance is often tipped in favor of doing everything for everyone else first. We often put our own needs and wants last. Doing this is not helpful to anyone in the long run!

Remember that you have rights as a family caregiver. Review these rights and internalize them. Let these strengthen and sustain you through the highs and lows.

∽

Caregiver Rights
As a family caregiver, I have the right to:

1. *Be shown respect, love, and acknowledgment for what I do for my loved ones.*
2. *Be proud of what I am doing and acknowledge the strength and perseverance it takes to consistently show up for my loved ones.*
3. *Look after my own needs. I will be able to care for my loved ones more effectively as a result.*
4. *Ask for and accept assistance from others.*
5. *Express and release difficult emotions like anger, frustration, and other negative emotions.*
6. *Disregard attempts made by others to control me through guilt or other manipulative means.*
7. *Not exhaust my own financial savings to bear the cost of my loved one's caregiving needs.*
8. *Preserve my autonomy and my right to build a life for myself that is separate from my caregiving role.*
9. *Outsource as many tasks as I can afford to enable me to maintain more balance.*
10. *Enjoy my own life and do things that bring me happiness without guilt.*

Neglecting yourself can lead to very serious consequences like burnout and must be prevented. Take proactive steps to address your physical, mental, and emotional needs. Don't push yourself to the limit and don't feel guilty focusing on yourself and your well-being. Taking care of yourself is a necessary component of being a loving and devoted caregiver to your aging parent.

"Caregiver Burnout and How to Address It" Summary Checklist

Reminders from this Bonus section:

1. Understand how dangerous caregiver burnout can be.
2. Recognize the signs of caregiver burnout and how to prevent it or stop its progression.
3. Find respite care if you're already in full burnout mode so you have dedicated time to recover.
4. Address your physical, mental, and emotional needs to prevent or recuperate from burnout.
5. Know and internalize the Caregiver Rights.

CONCLUSION

More and more people find themselves taking care of an aging loved one as the number of baby boomers and other seniors needing assistance continues to skyrocket. Taking care of a family member who is in need is an act of generosity, love, and service. Even if they are unable to express their gratitude, every day that you give your loved one the gift of your care and attention is of unparalleled importance and something that is worthy of accolades.

The time you have spent thinking about your aging loved one, preparing for how to be the best caregiver you can be, and even reading this book, shows your level of dedication and the depth of your love and compassion as a human being. You should be extremely proud of yourself and give yourself a big hug and pat on the back for all of your efforts and sacrifice. Your work is of the utmost importance to your loved one, your family tree, and our society at large. This is no exaggeration.

The family caregiver role is a role like no other. Like many family caregivers, you probably were ill-prepared for this situation to arise. But to be a competent family caregiver, you don't need to be a nursing prodigy, a superhuman, or a saint. You don't have to sacrifice your entire life to be able to give effective and loving care if you have the necessary knowledge, support, and tools. Your caregiver mindset will be the foundation of your entire journey. Safeguard and maintain this healthy mindset and the rest will be smoother sailing.

Just like in any other challenging endeavor, caregiving requires organization. By developing your organizational skills, you'll be better equipped to tackle your responsibilities and surmount any obstacle. Gathering all the relevant facts, and organizing a detailed plan of what needs to get done will significantly increase your confidence and reduce your stress.

Your Master Caregiving Checklist will become your trusted tool. This checklist will be your personal assistant keeping things organized and on track. Using this checklist will transform what used to feel like "juggling" to more "managing" and "maintaining." It turns things from overwhelming to organized and makes everything more objective and rational. Use it!

A certain level of caregiving knowledge can be learned just by reading books, but at some point, you need to get out there and research the specific resources and conditions that are specific to your situation and location. Don't let the research intimidate you. Use the tips in this book to guide your search queries and just start collecting the answers to the questions in the checklists.

Getting a firm understanding of your family's financial situation and all the possible sources of funds to support your loved one's caregiving needs will be instrumental in establishing a successful long-term care plan. Tackle this early on, as this information will drive many of the other decisions.

Once you decide on the best living arrangement for your loved one, you'll know what kind of care plan you'll need. Getting an understanding of how to look out for your loved one's overall health and well-being will give you more peace of mind.

Last but certainly not least, recognizing the importance of your own ongoing well-being in all aspects of your life will be critical to setting the right tone for the entire caregiving experience and beyond. Taking steps to nourish your body, mind, and spirit before, during, and after your caregiving journey will give you the best chance of providing the kind of care that you will look back on, be proud of, and have no regrets about.

Finally, when the caregiving journey comes to an end, you can look back on everything you have been through and know that you did the best job you could. That will give you a sense of peace that you will take with you for the rest of your days. And that peace is priceless.

APPENDIX

For digital versions of the resources in the Appendix, visit www. cynthiakaye.com.

RECAP OF THE 7 STEPS

Step 1: Accept Your New Role

Step 2: Gather the Facts and Get Organized

Step 3: Learn What Resources are Available

Step 4: Evaluate How to Pay for Care

Step 5: Decide on Living Arrangements and Related Care Plans

Step 6: Learn the Caregiving Basics

Step 7: Prioritize Self-Care

Step 1: Accept Your New Role

1. Know the signs when your parent is close to needing care and assistance.

2. Take steps to reframe your caregiver mindset: determine what's in and out of your control, recognize your self-worth, let go of harmful guilt and resentment, set realistic expectations on the length and scope of care, and try the Project-Into-the Future Exercise and realize that this caregiving season won't last forever.

Step 2: Gather the Facts and Get Organized

1. Use the Master Caregiver Checklist and gather all the facts about your aging parent's current situation across the major areas of their life, including medical, home safety, documents, and finances.

2. Review the list of caregiver duties that you'll be tackling.

3. Get the estate planning documents prepared.

4. Help your parent prepare an end-of-life plan.

5. Create a family plan.

6. Manage medical professionals with clear communication.

7. Add open times to your running Things I Need To Do section of the Master Caregiving Checklist.

8. Cross off the items on your running Things I Need To Do list as you accomplish them.

Step 3: Learn What Resources are Available

1. Familiarize yourself with the various government programs for seniors, such as Medicare, Medicaid, and

Social Security, to see if your aging loved one is eligible.

2. Spend time reviewing other senior and caregiver resources provided through various local and community organizations, such as adult day care programs and other community resources, to assist in multiple facets of a senior's daily life.

3. Review the education and support provided by online resources such as AARP.

4. Apply for any applicable programs to start the process and be diligent about following up. Government benefits are hard to get and easy to lose if you miss a filing or a deadline for a response. So, keep organized and stay on top of all deadlines.

5. Review the tips on being a long-distance caregiver if that applies to your situation.

Step 4: Evaluate How to Pay for Care

1. Research and understand the various funding sources to cover your aging parent's care needs.

2. Once you've applied for government benefits and researched private financing options, explore additional funding sources such as home sharing or downsizing.

3. Check with your employer for caregiver benefits, such as backup care services.

Step 5: Decide on Living Arrangements and Related Care Plan

1. Understand all of the available living arrangements for your parent and decide if using a senior housing referral agency makes sense for your family.

2. If your parent is aging in place, determine your in-home care plan, including whether you'll hire paid caregivers, recruit siblings, become the primary caregiver yourself, or a combination of these.
3. Review the difference between home care vs. home health and which of the two your parent will need.
4. Determine whether you'll hire caregivers directly or through a caregiving agency.
5. Know best practices for caregiver hiring, compensation, retention, and employment law.
6. Review tips on how to recruit family members and deal with difficult siblings.
7. Understand how you can get paid as a family caregiver.

Step 6: Learn the Caregiving Basics

1. Consider all aspects of your loved one's physical, cognitive, mental, and emotional health.
2. Get more knowledgeable about ADLs and IADLs and how these assessments are used to find help for your aging parent.
3. Learn how to communicate effectively with your aging loved one.
4. Understand the basics of dementia and related care.
5. Know the appropriate equipment and tools to make caregiving more efficient.
6. Recognize the difference between Quantity vs. Quality regarding time spent with your loved one.

Step 7: Prioritize Self-Care

1. Address and tend to your self-care pillars of maintaining your physical health, a healthy mindset

and mental health, and your emotional and spiritual health.

2. Practice self-care when dealing with different types of grief.

3. Rebuild your life when your caregiving journey ends.

Bonus : Caregiver Burnout and How to Address It

- Understand how dangerous caregiver burnout can be. Recognize the signs of caregiver burnout and how to
- prevent it or stop its progression.
- Find respite care if you're already in full burnout
- mode, so you have dedicated time to recover.
- Address your physical, mental, and emotional needs to
- prevent or recuperate from burnout.
- Know and internalize the Caregiver Bill of Rights.

MASTER CAREGIVER CHECKLIST

MASTER CAREGIVER CHECKLIST

MEDICAL INFORMATION

1. Primary Care Physician (Name, Address, Phone, Fax, Email):

_____
_____
_____

2. Specialty Doctor(s) (Name, Address, Phone, Fax, Email, Treating for what condition)

_____
_____
_____

3. Other Therapist(s) (Physical Therapist, Acupuncture, Speech Therapist, etc.) (Name, Address, Phone, Fax, Email)

_____
_____
_____

4. Closest Hospitals and Urgent Care Centers (Name, Address, Phone)

_____
_____
_____

5. List of Illnesses and Conditions

_____
_____
_____

6. History of Significant Treatments (surgeries, infusions, pain management, etc.)

_____
_____
_____

7. Medications, Supplements, and Vitamins List

Medication	Dosage/When to take	Purpose	Prescribing Doctor	Pharmacy Address/Phone

HOME SAFETY ASSESSMENT

Floors

☐ Remove unnecessary throw rugs or adhere them securely to the floor with double-sided tape or a non-slip rug mat.

☐ Remove any loose items on the floor, such as decoration items, baskets, magazines, or anything else that could be a trip hazard.

☐ Remove any plugs and lamp cords that are a trip hazard. Secure cords along the wall and out of the walking path.

☐ Rearrange furniture to make it as clear and open a walking path as possible.

Kitchen

☐ Rearrange the configuration of the kitchen items to make frequently used items within easy reach. Avoid putting anything on the top shelves of the cabinets to avoid the need for step stools.

☐ If step stools are unavoidable, get a sturdy step stool with a bar to hold on for more stability.

☐ Remove any rugs in the kitchen or securely fasten them to the ground with anti-slip rug mats.

☐ Consider swapping out easily breakable plates and glasses with non-breakable ones.

☐ Replace any burnt-out lightbulbs to ensure the kitchen is well-lit.

☐ Declutter any unnecessary items to minimize dust collection.

Bathrooms

☐ Install grab bars in the shower/tub and next to the toilet.

☐ Consider getting a tub transfer bench for over tub showers for less mobile loved ones.

☐ Place clean non-slip rubber mats on the shower/tub floor.

☐ Replace any burnt-out lightbulbs to ensure the bathroom is well-lit.

☐ Remove any toxic cleaning items that may be mistaken for shampoo, soap, or mouthwash.

Stairs

☐ Remove any loose items on the stairs.

☐ Replace any broken lightbulbs to ensure the staircase is well-lit.

☐ Install light switches at both the top and bottom of the stairs to ensure it is always well-lit.

☐ Repair any uneven surfaces or worn-out carpet on any step.

☐ Repair any unstable or loose handrails along the entire staircase.

☐ Consider getting a stair chair-lift installed once mobility becomes a serious enough issue.

Bedrooms/Closets

☐ Replace any burnt-out lightbulbs to ensure the bedrooms and closets are well-lit.

☐ Put a lamp with an easy on/off switch near the bed.

☐ Place a night light bright enough to light the path to the bathroom if your loved one needs to use the bathroom during the night.

☐ Remove any unnecessary rugs, cords, or other items on the ground to avoid trip hazards.

Porch, Entryway, and Garage

☐ Replace any burnt-out lightbulbs to ensure the porch, entryway, and garage are well-lit.

☐ Remove any overgrown plants, planters, and unnecessary items that may be a trip hazard on the porch and in the entryway or garage.

☐ Replace any frayed or worn-out welcome mats to minimize trip hazards.

☐ Declutter unnecessary items that collect dust and may be trip hazards throughout the areas.

In general

☐ Place an Emergency Contacts card in large print near each phone.

IMPORTANT DOCUMENTS AND CONTACTS

Documents for Assets and Liabilities

- ☐ Real estate documents (deeds, mortgage statements, HOA information)
- ☐ Bank accounts
- ☐ Retirement and investment accounts
- ☐ Insurance policies (home, auto, life, long term care)
- ☐ Pension/Retirement benefits
- ☐ Online social media and other accounts (login information)
- ☐ Credit Card and outstanding loan statements
- ☐ Auto ownership documents
- ☐ Jewelry, art, or other collectibles
- ☐ Business or corporate assets

Documents for End of Life Planning

- ☐ Living Trust
- ☐ Pourover Will
- ☐ Power of Attorney for Health
- ☐ Power of Attorney for Finances
- ☐ Funeral plan and burial plot documents

Other Important Legal Documents

- ☐ Birth certificate, marriage certificates, citizenship papers, military discharge papers, divorce certificates, and death certificates of a spouse

Important Contacts

Anyone named in their estate planning docs (in the trust or will):

_____

_____

Beneficiaries of their retirement accounts, annuity or insurance policies:

_____

_____

Attorney and Executor/Trustee:

_____

_____

Family members to keep updated:

_____

_____

Close friends:

_____

_____

Social and religious organizations:

_____

_____

FINANCES/PERSONAL EXPENSES AND BILLS

Item	Current Monthly Amount	New Budgeted Monthly Amount
Housing		
Mortgage/Rent		
HOA		
Home Insurance		
Property tax		
Gardener		
Other		
Utilities		
Electricity		
Water/Sewer		
Gas		
Trash		
Phone		
Internet		
Other subscriptions (Netflix, magazines, Amazon Prime, etc.)		
Food/Clothing/Grooming/Goods		
Food/Grocery		
Clothing		
Grooming (hair, nails, etc.)		
Household supplies (cleaning, laundry)		

Item	Current Monthly Amount	New Budgeted Monthly Amount
Medical/Health		
Medical insurance		
Co-pays		
Prescriptions		
Supplements		
Treatments		
Auto/Transportation		
Car payments		
Car insurance		
Registration & license		
Other Insurance		
Life insurance premiums		
Long-term care premiums		
Other		
Debt Payments		
Credit card and other debt payments		
Hired Helpers		
Current caregivers		
Housekeepers		
Handymen		
Miscellaneous		
Entertainment/Vacations		
Gifts		
Dues/Donations (assn fees, church tithing, etc.)		
Leisure spending (buying trinkets, collectibles, etc.)		

202 Master Caregiver Checklist

ADL Assessment (Activities of Daily Living)

Bathing
- ☐ Independently showers or bathes (3 points)
- ☐ Needs some assistance getting in/out of shower or reaching certain body areas (2 points)
- ☐ Needs full or almost full assistance getting dressed (1 point)

Dressing
- ☐ Independently dresses (3 points)
- ☐ Needs some assistance getting dressed (2 points)
- ☐ Needs full or almost full assistance getting dressed (1 point)

Continence
- ☐ Has complete control over urination and defecation (3 points)
- ☐ Is having noticeable accidents during daytime and/or nighttime (2 points)
- ☐ Is completely or almost completely unable to control bladder or bower (1 point)

Transferring (getting in/out of bed, chairs and other furniture)
- ☐ Independently walks from Point A to Point B and can get in/out of furniture without help (3 points)
- ☐ Needs some assistance transferring such as holding on to grab bars or uses a cane (2 points)
- ☐ Needs full or almost full assistance transferring (1 point)

Feeding (not including meal prep)
- ☐ Independently eats without help (3 points)
- ☐ Needs some assistance with feeding such as need food cut into small pieces (2 points)
- ☐ Needs full or almost full assistance getting spoon from table to mouth (1 point)

Toileting
- ☐ Independently uses toilet and cleans self without help (3 points)
- ☐ Needs some assistance transferring to toilet (2 points)
- ☐ Needs full or almost full assistance toileting and having their genital area cleaned (1 point)

Add up Total Points: _____ (any score below 13 should trigger a further evaluation with your loved one's medical team to see if increase assistance is needed)

IADL Assessment (Instrumental Activities of Daily Living)

Laundry
- ☐ Independently manages own laundry (3 points)
- ☐ Needs some assistance with laundry (2 points)
- ☐ Is unable to do their own laundry at all (1 point)

Cleaning/Housekeeping
- ☐ Independently manages keeping home clean (3 points)
- ☐ Needs some assistance with daily chores (2 points)
- ☐ Is unable to maintain basic cleanliness on their own (1 point)

Medication Management
- ☐ Independently manages taking correct medications on schedule (3 points)
- ☐ Needs some assistance preparing and distributing medications but takes them responsibly on their own (2 points)
- ☐ Is unable to responsibly take medications on their own (1 point)

Money Management
- ☐ Independently manages monthly budget and finances without help (3 points)
- ☐ Needs some assistance with banking and making major purchases (2 points)
- ☐ Is unable to handle money or pay bills on their own (1 point)

Transportation
- ☐ Independently travels (drives car or public transport) without help (3 points)
- ☐ Cannot drive but can still take public transportation without help (2 points)
- ☐ Is unable to drive or take public transport on their own (1 point)

Communication
- ☐ Independently able to use telephone, cell phone and/or internet (3 points)
- ☐ Needs some assistance or guidance with the phone or internet (2 points)
- ☐ Is unable to use the phone or internet at all on their own (1 point)

Shopping
- ☐ Independently shops for groceries and necessities without help (3 points)
- ☐ Needs some assistance or guidance with shopping (2 points)
- ☐ Is unable to shop at all on their own (1 point)

Meal Prep
- ☐ Independently able to plan, prep and cook meals (3 points)
- ☐ Needs some assistance planning, preparing or cooking meals (2 points)
- ☐ Unable to plan, prep or cook meals at all on their own (1 point)

Add up Total Points: _____ (any score below 18 should trigger a further evaluation with your loved one's medical team to see if increase assistance is needed)

MEALS AND ERRANDS

Breakfast routine (time of day, common items enjoyed, source of food/grocery store):

Notes (observations, etc.):

Lunch routine (time of day, common items enjoyed, source of food/grocery store):

Notes (observations, etc.):

Dinner routine (time of day, common items enjoyed, source of food/grocery store):

Notes (observations, etc.):

Snack routine (time of day, common items enjoyed, source of food/grocery store):

Notes (observations, etc.):

Dietary restrictions:

Notes (observations, etc.):

Routine Errands (type of errand, who currently handles):

Notes (observations, etc.):

HOUSING AND CARE PLAN

Discuss which of the following living arrangements would make the most sense for your loved one. Note the pros/cons of each and the preferred type of care (such as private in-home caregivers vs. group caregivers at a chosen facility). Research the chosen options.

Stay at home (discuss potential downsizing or getting a roommate):

Notes (observations, etc.):

_____
_____
_____

Move in with family:

Notes (observations, etc.):

_____
_____
_____

Move to a Senior Independent Living Community:

Notes (observations, etc.):

_____
_____
_____

Move to an Assisted Living Facility:

Notes (observations, etc.):

_____
_____
_____

Move to a Continuing Care Retirement Community:

Notes (observations, etc.):

_____
_____
_____

Move to a Skilled Nursing Facility:

Notes (observations, etc.):

_____
_____
_____

Sample Family Plan

Family Members

- Name, Phone, Email: _____
- Name, Phone, Email: _____
- Name, Phone, Email: _____
- Name, Phone, Email: _____

Example Caregiving Tasks Responsibility Chart (Version 1: divided by tasks):

Caregiving Task	Name of Family Member #1	Name of Family Member #2	Name of Family Member #3	Name of Family Member #4
Example: Managing doctor appointments (over the phone)	✓			
Errands: grocery shopping and weekly laundry		✓		
Driving: take to medical and physical therapy appointments	✓			
Manage paid caregiver schedules and payment			✓	
Financial support: send money each month to cover paid caregivers			✓	✓

Example Caregiving Tasks Responsibility Chart (Version 2: divided by days of the week):

	Sun	Mon	Tue	Wed	Thu	Fri	Sat
					Caregiving Schedule		
6:00 AM	Allen (7am to 10pm)(15 hrs)	Paid Caregiver-Jenny (6am-2pm)(8 hrs)	Paid Caregiver-Jenny (7am-9pm)(14 hrs)	Richard (7am-6pm)(11 hrs)	Paid Caregiver-Jenny (6am-2pm)(8 hrs)	Paid Caregiver-Jenny (6am-6pm)(12 hrs)	Richard (7am-10pm)(15 hrs)
7:00 AM							
8:00 AM							
9:00 AM							
10:00 AM							
11:00 AM							
12:00 PM							
1:00 PM							
2:00 PM		Carol (2pm to OVERNIGHT)			Richard (2pm to 10pm)(8 hrs)		
3:00 PM							
4:00 PM							
5:00 PM							
6:00 PM							
7:00 PM							
8:00 PM						Carol (6pm to OVERNIGHT)	
9:00 PM			9pm bed	Carol (6pm to OVERNIGHT)			
10:00 PM	10pm bed				10pm bed		10pm bed
11:00 PM							
OVERNIGHT							

RESOURCES AND BENEFITS RESEARCH WORKSHEET

Government Resources

(Research and Jot Notes on Eligibility Requirements Applicable to Your Situation)

Medicare (medicare.gov):

_____

_____

_____

Medicaid (state-specific):

_____

_____

_____

Social Security (ssa.gov):

_____

_____

_____

Administration on Aging (link):

_____

_____

_____

Department of Veterans Affairs (va.gov):

_____

_____

_____

The Americans with Disabilities Act National Network (link):

_____

_____

_____

MedlinePlus (medlineplus.gov):

_____

_____

_____

Long Term Care Ombudsman Program (state-specific):

_____

_____

_____

Local and Community Resources

(Check these resources on any special free or discounted benefits for seniors)

Transportation Resources (Dial-a-Rides, etc.):

_____
_____
_____

Social Centers (Senior Centers, Churches, Libraries):

_____
_____
_____

Legal Services (Legal Aid):

_____
_____
_____

Food & Nutrition Programs (Meals on Wheels, etc.):

_____
_____
_____

Adult Day Care Programs:

_____
_____
_____

EMERGENCY CONTACT LIST

In case of emergency, call 911.

Police Department: _____

Fire Department: _____

Closest Hospital: _____

Primary Care Physician: _____

Family Members:

Family Member 1 (name and contact): _____

Family Member 2 (name and contact): _____

Family Member 3 (name and contact): _____

Family Member 4 (name and contact): _____

Family Member 5 (name and contact): _____

Close Neighbors:

Neighbor 1 (name and contact): _____

Neighbor 2 (name and contact): _____

Neighbor 3 (name and contact): _____

Neighbor 4 (name and contact): _____

Neighbor 4 (name and contact): _____

ONLINE ACCOUNTS INFORMATION

Social Media & Email Accounts (Facebook, YouTube, etc.):

Company Website	Username	Password	Acct # / Notes
Facebook.com	John Doe	123XYZ	
Gmail.com	johndoe@gmail.com	234XYZ	

Financial Accounts (bank accounts, stock brokerage accounts, insurance accounts, etc.):

Company Website	Username	Password	Acct # / Note
Ex: Chase Bank	JohnDoe01	345XYZ	#00000

Other Accounts (utilities, Netflix, Amazon, etc.):

Company Website	Username	Password	Acct # / Note
Ex: AT&T (phone bill)	JohnDoe345	345XYZ	#00000

THINGS I HAVE TO DO:

- ☐ _____
- ☐ _____
- ☐ _____
- ☐ _____
- ☐ _____
- ☐ _____
- ☐ _____
- ☐ _____
- ☐ _____
- ☐ _____
- ☐ _____
- ☐ _____
- ☐ _____
- ☐ _____
- ☐ _____
- ☐ _____
- ☐ _____
- ☐ _____
- ☐ _____
- ☐ _____
- ☐ _____

END OF LIFE CHECKLIST AND PLAN TEMPLATE

End-of-Life Checklist and Plan Template

ESTATE PLAN CHECKLIST

Get these 4 Main Estate Planning Documents in Place

Revocable Living Trust: this lists all of your loved one's assets and which people or organizations will receive each asset.

Pourover Will: this document ensures that any assets that weren't previously included in the individual's trust will auto-transfer to the trust upon their death (this is to avoid an otherwise long and inefficient court probate process).

Durable Power of Attorney for Financial Matters: this document selects a financial agent to make important financial decisions for the loved one when they cannot do so themselves.

Advance Directive for Healthcare: this document selects an agent to make important medical decisions for the loved one when they cannot do so themselves and indicates your loved one's medical treatment preferences.

Review Beneficiaries and Digital Asset Decisions

Verify the beneficiaries for all assets not included in the trust, such as:
- Life insurance policies
- Pensions
- 401(k) and IRA/investment accounts

Verify instructions for your loved one's digital assets (social media accounts, online accounts, blogs, etc.)
- List out all digital assets/online accounts and related log-in credentials (usernames and passwords, including any keys to cryptocurrency wallets)
- Understand your loved one's preferences, if any, for what to do with these digital assets after the passing of your loved one.
- Consider adding a digital executor in your loved one's trust to manage these digital assets after the loved one's death, as applicable.

NOTES:_____

_____

_____

_____

_____

_____

_____

_____

END-OF-LIFE PLAN TEMPLATE

- Revocable Living Trust:
  Physical copy located _____ (Link to Digital Copy: _____)

- Pourover Will:
  Physical copy located _____ (Link to Digital Copy: _____)

- Durable Financial Power of Attorney:
  Physical copy located _____ (Link to Digital Copy: _____)

- Advance Medical Directive:
  Physical copy located _____ (Link to Digital Copy: _____)

- Life Insurance policies:
  - Insurer name and phone, Amount Insured, Beneficiaries:
    _____

    - Physical copy located _____ (Link to Digital Copy: _____)

  - Insurer name and phone, Amount Insured, Beneficiaries:
    _____

    - Physical copy located _____ (Link to Digital Copy: _____)

- Pension(s)
  - Pension administrator name and phone, Amount of Benefits, Beneficiaries:
    _____

    - Physical copy located _____ (Link to Digital Copy: _____)

- 401(k) and IRA/investment accounts
  - Brokerage/Account administrator name and phone, Balance,
    Beneficiaries:_____

    - Physical copy located _____ (Link to Digital Copy: _____)

- Brokerage/Account administrator name and phone, Balance,
  Beneficiaries:_____

  - Physical copy located _____ (Link to Digital Copy: _____)

- Digital Asset/Online Accounts
  - Account type, website address, log-in username and password:
    _____

- Digital Asset/Online Accounts
  - Account type, website address, log-in username and password:
    _____

FUNERAL ARRANGEMENTS CHECKLIST

Before Death

- Check if any prepaid funeral plan or burial plot has been purchased and review the contracts.
- If not, consider doing a prepaid funeral plan and purchasing a burial plot to have one less thing to worry about when that time comes.
- One benefit of pre-planning is you can know your loved one's desires and preferences (e.g., what burial clothing and accessories they want, do they want an open or closed casket or viewing before the cremation, what personal items would they like included in their urn if cremated, who do they want to invite to the service, what music and photos do they want in the service, what casket or urn material do they prefer, etc.). If this is too sensitive in light of your loved one's condition, you can use your judgment and skip these details. Everyone has a different level of sensitivity to these matters, so use your discernment.
- Gather information you will need for the Death Certificate (social security number, date of birth, place of work - name, address, occupation, full names of the deceased's parents)
- Gather a list of names and contact info of the people to be invited to the memorial service.
- Gather favorite songs, readings, and photos to be played and displayed at the service.

After Death

- Notify the authorities (911 or local emergency numbers) to report the death if not in a hospital or nursing facility.
- Notify close family and friends.
- Contact the funeral director to report the death.
- Confirm the responsible party for billing purposes if not yet paid for.
- Provide information for the Death Certificate to the funeral director (social security number, date of birth, place of work - name, address, occupation, full names of the deceased's parents)
- Decide on burial clothing and accessories for viewing and traditional burials. For cremation, decide on personal items you may want to include with the ashes in the urn.
- Decide on the type of burial desired (in-ground vs. above-ground burial, vault, mausoleum, cremation-discuss these options with the funeral director)
- Select the type of casket or container (wood, metal, wicker, cardboard, urn)
- Open or closed casket for the funeral service
- Decide on whether you will have a funeral service and related details (before or after the cremation, at the funeral home, church, graveside, or home, etc.)
- Prepare the obituary (vital statistics, hobbies, career path, memberships, and associations)
- Prepare the memorial service program (framed photos, program pamphlet, readings, songs, slideshows).
- Decide who will give the eulogy (clergy, family, friends, combination).
- Work with the funeral home to select flower arrangements for the service.
- Work with the funeral home to select music for the service (prepare a list of favorite songs of the deceased loved one).
- Arrange pallbearers (4-6 men usually, friends or relatives but usually not next of kin).
- Work with the funeral home to confirm transportation of guests from the funeral service to the gravesite (personal cars vs. a shuttle provided by the funeral home).
- Select a grave marker (if not already done in a pre-paid plan).
- Notify friends and family of the funeral service.
- Decide whether to have a wake prior to the service or a reception after the service and where and when to hold this gathering (at a restaurant, funeral home, church, home, etc.).
- Consider how to help accommodate out-of-town guests coming for the funeral (help with travel plans, airport transfers, lodging, etc.)

OTHER TEMPLATES

~

This section includes some more helpful samples and templates. For digital versions of these and any other resource in the Appendix, visit www.cynthiakaye.com.

~

Sample Caregiver Interview Questions

- Why do you want to be a caregiver?
- In your opinion, what makes a good caregiver?
- Do you fit the descriptions above? How?
- What makes you most eager to work with seniors?
- Can you tell me about a personal or work-related goal you have? How do you plan to accomplish those goals?
- What are your short-term and long-term plans?
- What other commitments do you have that may interfere with your ability to be a caregiver?
- What aspects of caregiving do you dislike the most?
- What motivates you when you have work challenges?
- What kind of problem-solver are you? Can you describe a time you had to be creative in solving a problem?
- If hired, what is the first thing you would do?
- What would you do if you were alone with the care recipient and they fell on the ground and possibly fractured a bone?
- Do you have reliable transportation and a clean driving record?
- How would your friends and prior co-workers or bosses describe you?
- How do you handle patients who refuse to eat, bathe, or cooperate?
- Do you have experience working with people with dementia? What are some particular things you do to care for those with memory issues?
- Are you comfortable meal-planning and cooking and generally managing a tidy household on your own?
- Why did you leave your last job?
- What would you do if your shift has ended but your replacement has not yet arrived?

Sample Family Caregiver Agreement

FAMILY CAREGIVER SERVICES AGREEMENT

This agreement made this ___ day of _____, 20__, by and between [FULL NAME(S) OF CARE RECIPIENT(S)] (hereafter referred to as "Care Recipient(s)"), and [FULL NAME OF CAREGIVER], Caregiver (hereafter referred to as "Caregiver"). In consideration of the mutual promises contained herein, the parties agree as follows:

1. **Nutrition.** Caregiver will prepare meals, grocery shop, and assist with feeding, as needed.
2. **Housekeeping.** Caregiver shall maintain the home in a clean and orderly condition. Caregiver will purchase any necessary cleaning supplies and will be reimbursed for such expenses.
3. **Assistance outside the Home.** Caregiver will run errands including picking up medications, grocery shopping, and, if applicable, maintaining Care Recipients' car.
4. **Personal Care Needs.** Caregiver will observe the physical and mental states of the Care Recipients on a regular basis, and make arrangements with applicable physicians or medical staff. Caregiver will assist in carrying out the instructions of physicians including helping with medication management. Caregiver will also help Care Recipient(s) with bathing, dressing, toileting, hair care, shaving, eating, care of clothing, personal shopping and incidental services, as needed.
5. **Transportation.** Caregiver will assist with transportation needs by driving or arranging for Uber or other appropriate transportation methods.
6. **Compensation.** Care Recipients will pay Caregiver an hourly rate of $[20] per hour. The initial planned schedule will be for Caregiver to work [40] hours per week, for a weekly pay of [$800] per week, with the first payment to be due starting on _____. Payments may reflect higher or lower amounts based on the actual number of hours worked that week (based on a weekly log of actual hours worked to be kept by Caregiver). Payments may be made by cash, check, Venmo, or bank transfers or any other method mutually agreed upon by the parties.
7. **Termination; Governing Law, Entirety of Agreement and Severability.** This agreement will continue until terminated in writing by any of the parties. This agreement shall be governed by the laws of the State of _____. It constitutes the entire agreement between the parties regarding its subject matter. If any provision in this contract is held by any court to be invalid, void or unenforceable, the remaining provisions shall nevertheless continue in full force and effect.

THIS IS A LEGALLY BINDING CONTRACT. EACH PARTY HAS READ THE ABOVE AGREEMENT BEFORE SIGNING IT. EACH PARTY UNDERSTANDS THE AGREEMENT THAT HE OR SHE IS MAKING. We, the Care Recipient(s) and Caregiver having read this agreement, agree to its terms and sign it as our free act as of the date signed below.

_____   _____
[FULL NAME] (Care Recipient)   [FULL NAME]   (Care Recipient)

Date: _____   Date: _____

_____
[FULL NAME] (Caregiver)

Date: _____

TEMPLATE: CAREGIVER HOURS LOG

Week of _____	# of hours worked this week: _____. circle days worked: Sun M T W Th F Sat
Week of _____	# of hours worked this week: _____. circle days worked: Sun M T W Th F Sat
Week of _____	# of hours worked this week: _____. circle days worked: Sun M T W Th F Sat
Week of _____	# of hours worked this week: _____. circle days worked: Sun M T W Th F Sat
Week of _____	# of hours worked this week: _____. circle days worked: Sun M T W Th F Sat
Week of _____	# of hours worked this week: _____. circle days worked: Sun M T W Th F Sat
Week of _____	# of hours worked this week: _____. circle days worked: Sun M T W Th F Sat
Week of _____	# of hours worked this week: _____. circle days worked: Sun M T W Th F Sat
Week of _____	# of hours worked this week: _____. circle days worked: Sun M T W Th F Sat
Week of _____	# of hours worked this week: _____. circle days worked: Sun M T W Th F Sat
Week of _____	# of hours worked this week: _____. circle days worked: Sun M T W Th F Sat
Week of _____	# of hours worked this week: _____. circle days worked: Sun M T W Th F Sat
Week of _____	# of hours worked this week: _____. circle days worked: Sun M T W Th F Sat
Week of _____	# of hours worked this week: _____. circle days worked: Sun M T W Th F Sat
Week of _____	# of hours worked this week: _____. circle days worked: Sun M T W Th F Sat
Week of _____	# of hours worked this week: _____. circle days worked: Sun M T W Th F Sat
Week of _____	# of hours worked this week: _____. circle days worked: Sun M T W Th F Sat
Week of _____	# of hours worked this week: _____. circle days worked: Sun M T W Th F Sat
Week of _____	# of hours worked this week: _____. circle days worked: Sun M T W Th F Sat
Week of _____	# of hours worked this week: _____. circle days worked: Sun M T W Th F Sat
Week of _____	# of hours worked this week: _____. circle days worked: Sun M T W Th F Sat
Week of _____	# of hours worked this week: _____. circle days worked: Sun M T W Th F Sat

Sample "Seeking Roommate" Listing

Seeking [Female][Male] Housemate in 4 Bedroom House for my Elderly Parent

We have a bright and large yet cozy bedroom on the second floor of a 2-story townhouse in a quiet neighborhood in [CITY NAME] (adjacent to [LARGE NEIGHBORING CITY] and conveniently near both the ___ freeway). The bedroom is one of four bedrooms in the townhouse where my elderly [mother][father] lives. The bedroom has a queen bed, large desk, free Wi-Fi, closet space, and a large window. This bedroom shares a full bath with whoever is staying in the other adjacent bedrooms (adult kids or caregivers of my elderly mom who may be staying the night).

*We are seeking a friendly, mature, clean, polite, and responsible FEMALE housemate.
*Non-smoker, no alcohol, no drug use, no loud music, no guests
*Rent includes 1 private room and shared full bathroom
*1 outdoor dedicated parking spot
*Private microwave and mini-fridge in-room, generally no access to main kitchen

RENT:
The rent for this room is [$750] per month.
Month-to-Month Lease Term

NEIGHBORHOOD:
The neighborhood is quiet and conveniently located close (5-minute walk) to lots of shops (e.g. pharmacy, restaurants, Burger King, Starbucks, diners, brand new luxury residences and commercial developments, public library, fitness centers, etc.) and bus stops. It's also about a 10-minute drive to the ___ freeway and right next to [Large Neighboring City] (with [list a few attractions of your neighboring large city]) and a 15-minute drive to [another large city] and 30 minutes to downtown [main downtown area name].

Looking forward to connecting and thank you so much!

Sample Rental Agreement

Rental Agreement for Room in a Private Home

This Agreement is between [PRIMARY CAREGIVER'S NAME, IF PROPERTY IS UNDER YOUR NAME OR YOU ARE THE POWER OF ATTORNEY, OR YOUR LOVED ONE, IF PROPERTY IS UNDER THEIR NAME] (Property Provider) and [ROOMMATE'S FULL LEGAL NAME] (Tenant) for the rental of a furnished/unfurnished (circle one) room with a shared/private (circle one) bathroom located at [PROPERTY ADDRESS] (Property). Tenant will move in on [MOVE-IN DATE] and will continue to stay on a month-to-month basis until either party terminates this Agreement upon 30 days prior written notice, unless otherwise agreed to in writing by Tenant and Property Provider. Tenant must move out upon the effective date of termination of this Agreement.

The monthly rent is $____ (or daily prorated rate of $____ for future partial months, if any), payable on the ___ST day of each month/rental period. Rent includes all utilities (power, gas, water, trash, internet). [ALTER AS NEEDED; IT'S GENERALLY EASIER TO JUST INCLUDE ALL UTILITIES AND REFLECT THE INCREASED COSTS OF UTILITIES IN THE MONTHLY RENT]

A security deposit of $____ (due upon signing this Agreement) shall be refunded by Property Provider upon Tenant's move-out, less any appropriate and reasonable charges for cleaning and/or for damages caused by Tenant.

With 30 calendar days written notice to Tenant, Property Provider may raise the rent, alter the terms of the Agreement, or terminate the tenancy. Conversely, the Tenant must give Property Provider 30 days prior written notice of intent to terminate the tenancy.

Property Provider and Tenant agree to honor the following House Rules and any additional written Rules attached [REVISE AS DESIRED]: light cooking is allowed only in the kitchen, reasonable use of laundry facilities is allowed provided Tenant promptly removes items from the laundry area (Property Provider may move Tenant's laundry items from washer to dryer to basket as needed), no guests/overnight guests allowed without prior permission from Property Provider, no subletting or assignment allowed without prior consent from Property Provider, no smoking/drugs/alcohol/loud noises, music or illegal activities on premises, no entering non-common areas (e.g., other bedrooms or bathrooms) without prior permission, please remember to lock the door upon entering/exiting the home, please take off shoes before entering home, please conserve energy (turn off lights/fans when leaving room, etc.), no sharing/copying key with anyone else, no flushing anything other than toilet paper down the toilets, take your trash out of your room regularly, no open flames/candles in your room, no cooking devices or other fire hazards in your room, be generally respectful of privacy and courteous to fellow housemates (including any other renters, as applicable), no alterations, additions and/or modifications to property without prior permission from Property Provider (e.g., painting, fixtures, etc.), no pets please.

Room Maintenance and Privacy: Tenant shall maintain the room in a safe, clean and sanitary condition. Tenant will advise Property Provider promptly of any problem (leaky faucet, etc.) discovered by Tenant. Other than in emergency situations, Property Provider may enter room to initiate repairs after giving Tenant reasonable advance notice. Cleaning services are not included.

In case of emergency, Tenant authorizes Property Provider to contact:
Name/Relationship: _____ Phone: _____
Name/Relationship: _____ Phone: _____

The undersigned have read and understand the foregoing Agreement and acknowledge receipt of a copy. Except as otherwise stated herein, any changes to this Agreement must be done in writing signed by both parties.

Tenant Signature: Property Provider Signature:
Signed: _____   Signed: _____
Name: _____   Name: _____
Date: _____   Date: _____
Cell Phone #: _____   Cell Phone #: _____
Email: _____   Email: _____

PLEASE REVIEW MY BOOK

YOU CAN MAKE A DIFFERENCE

Did you get value out of this book? You can make a big difference!

Honest reviews on Amazon will help bring this book to the attention of other readers and caregivers who can also benefit from this information.

If you enjoyed this book and found it to be helpful, I would be very grateful if you could spend a minute to leave it an honest review. It can be as short and sweet as you'd like and it will make a huge difference.

Thank you very much!

~CK

ACKNOWLEDGMENTS

I would like to acknowledge the tremendous debt I owe to my incredibly supportive husband Ted and our sons, Matthew, Ryan, and Nicky. They've put up with me spending every spare moment in front of my computer during the creation of this book and I appreciate their patience and support immensely.

I would also like to thank the following people who helped edit and refine this book: my husband Ted, my brother Peter, my dear friend Tina Park, and my incredible early reader Jackie MacHardy, who provided tremendously helpful feedback and edits to improve the book.

Last but not least, I would like to extend my deepest gratitude to my mom and dad, Winnie and Kenneth, whose love and encouragement have always been a great source of inspiration. Dad, I love you, miss you dearly, and think of you every day. Mom, your youthful spirit, beauty, and strength inspire me so much. Thank you for your unconditional love.

ABOUT THE AUTHOR

Cynthia Kaye is an attorney, wife, mother, entrepreneur, and caregiver to her beloved parents. Cynthia has over ten years of experience as a family caregiver to her aging parents, having cared for her late father who suffered a stroke and was wheelchair-bound and bedridden during the time leading up to his passing. Cynthia not only learned a lot from her own caregiving experiences, but she has always had a heart for all seniors and the caregivers who take care of them. She personally connects with those who are going through the difficult and often lonely journey of caring for their elderly loved ones and is passionate about sharing any knowledge and tips to improve their lives. Cynthia lives in Southern California with her husband and three sons and loves to work in her vegetable garden when she has any free time.

BIBLIOGRAPHY

10 Things to Consider Before Becoming Your Parent's Caregiver. (2017, June 16). ARAG Legal. Retrieved September 23, 2022, from https://www.araglegal. com/individuals/learning-center/topics/caring-for-others/ten-things-to-consider-as-parents-caregiver

Wells, B. (2022, January 19). *A Caregiver's Guide to ADLs and IADLs.* My Caring Plan. Retrieved September 23, 2022, from https://www.mycaringplan.com/blog/adls-and-iadls/

Caregiving 101: On Being a Caregiver. (2022, July 20). Family Caregiver Alliance. Retrieved September 23, 2022, from https://www.caregiver.org/resource/caregiving-101-being-caregiver/

The Mindset of a Caregiver | UK Human Resources. (n.d.). Retrieved September 23, 2022, from https://www.uky.edu/hr/thrive/03-09-2016/mindset-caregiver

Caregiver Depression: A Silent Health Crisis. (2021, July 15). Family Caregiver Alliance. Retrieved September 23, 2022, from https://www.caregiver.org/resource/caregiver-depression-silent-health-crisis/

Stroke Recovery: Tips for the Caregiver. (2010, March 30). WebMD. Retrieved September 23, 2022, from https://www.webmd.com/stroke/features/stroke-recovery-tips-for-the-caregiver#:%7E:text=Caregivers%20often%20need%20to%3A,manage%20finances%20and%20insurance%20coverage

Frequently Asked Questions About Caregiving. (n.d.). National Institute on Aging. Retrieved September 23, 2022, from https://www.nia.nih.gov/health/frequently-asked-questions-about-caregiving#new

Huntsberry-Lett, A. (2021, October 28). *Caregiver Statistics: Facts About Family Caregivers.* © 2007-2022 AgingCare All Rights Reserved. Retrieved

September 23, 2022, from https://www.agingcare.com/articles/who-are-family-caregivers-459287.htm

Adams, T. (2021, July 22). *5 Signs Your Aging Parent Needs Help*. Brandon Wilde. Retrieved September 23, 2022, from https://www.brandonwilde.com/blog/signs-aging-parents-need-help/

10 Signs Your Parents Need Assistance To Safely Live At Home. (2020, November 12). Georgetown Home Care. Retrieved September 23, 2022, from https://www.georgetownhomecare.com/10-signs-your-parents-need-assistance-to-safely-live-at-home/

In Home Supportive Services. (n.d.). Retrieved September 23, 2022, from https://www.cdss.ca.gov/in-home-supportive-services

How Medicaid Can Help with Medical Expenses for Seniors. (2022, August 24). Family Caregiver Alliance. Retrieved September 23, 2022, from https://www.caregiver.org/news/how-medicaid-can-help-medical-expenses-seniors/

How Social Security Benefits Work. (2021, October 15). Investopedia. Retrieved September 23, 2022, from https://www.investopedia.com/terms/s/social-security-benefits.asp#:%7E:text=Social%20Security%20benefits%20provide%20partial,order%20to%20qualify%20for%20benefits.

Apply for Retirement Benefits | SSA. (n.d.). Retrieved September 23, 2022, from https://www.ssa.gov/benefits/retirement/apply.html#:%7E:text=You%20can%20apply%20up%20to,you%20can%+https://www.aarp.org/caregiving/home-care/info-2017/adult-day-care.html20apply%20in%20August.

Kiger, B. . P. J. (n.d.). *Adult Day Care: What Family Caregivers Need to Know*. AARP. Retrieved September 23, 2022, from https://www.aarp.org/caregiving/home-care/info-2017/adult-day-care.html

Adult Day Care: How to Support a Resistant Parent. (n.d.). A Place for Mom. Retrieved September 23, 2022, from https://www.aplaceformom.com/caregiver-resources/articles/adult-day-care

7 Sources of Free Legal Services for Seniors. (2022, May 6). DailyCaring. Retrieved September 23, 2022, from https://dailycaring.com/7-sources-of-free-legal-services-for-seniors/

What Is a Geriatric Care Manager? (n.d.). National Institute on Aging. Retrieved September 23, 2022, from https://www.nia.nih.gov/health/what-geriatric-care-manager

Getting Started with Long-Distance Caregiving. (n.d.). National Institute on Aging. Retrieved September 23, 2022, from https://www.nia.nih.gov/health/getting-started-long-distance-caregiving

American Association of Retired Persons | American organization. (n.d.). Encyclopedia Britannica. Retrieved September 23, 2022, from https://www.britannica.com/topic/American-Association-of-Retired-Persons

Paying for Care. (n.d.). National Institute on Aging. Retrieved September 23, 2022, from https://www.nia.nih.gov/health/paying-care

Senior Homeshares: Homeshare for 60+. (n.d.). Senior Homeshares. Retrieved September 23, 2022, from https://www.seniorhomeshares.com/about

RetireGuide, LLC. (2022, August 2). *A Seniors Guide to Downsizing For Retirement.* RetireGuide. Retrieved September 23, 2022, from https://www.retireguide.com/guides/downsizing-for-retirement/

Reverse Mortgage: The Pros and Cons. (2022, June 22). Investopedia. Retrieved September 23, 2022, from https://www.investopedia.com/reverse-mortgage-pros-and-cons-5209641#:%7E:text=Your%20spouse%20is%2062%20or%20older&text=That%20means%20no%20more%20credit,might%20be%20a%20good%20choice.

Varkala, I. (2022, July 18). *A Guide To Caring For Elderly Parents.* AgingInPlace.org. Retrieved September 23, 2022, from https://agingin place.org/a-guide-to-caring-for-elderly-parents/

Residential Facilities, Assisted Living, and Nursing Homes. (n.d.). National Institute on Aging. Retrieved September 23, 2022, from https://www.nia.nih.gov/health/residential-facilities-assisted-living-and-nursing-homes

Avenue, N. (2020, September 25). *The Disadvantages Of Aging In Place*. Forbes. Retrieved September 23, 2022, from https://www.forbes.com/sites/nextav enue/2020/09/25/the-disadvantages-of-aging-in-place/?sh=703fddf1b307

AgeInPlace.com. (2018, December 30). *What is Aging in Place? - Age in Place Definition*. Aging in Place. Retrieved September 23, 2022, from https://agein place.com/aging-in-place-basics/what-is-aging-in-place/#:%7E:text= Aging%20in%20place% 20is%20a,time%20as%20their%20needs%20change.

Residential Facilities, Assisted Living, and Nursing Homes. (n.d.-b). National Institute on Aging. Retrieved September 23, 2022, from https://www.nia. nih.gov/health/residential-facilities-assisted-living-and-nursing-homes

Hicks, K. (2020, October 14). *Pros and Cons of Aging in Place*. SeniorAdvisor.com Blog. Retrieved September 23, 2022, from https://www.senioradvisor.com/ blog/2016/06/pros-and-cons-of-aging-in-place/

Avenue, N. (2022, August 3). *6 Ways to Improve the Situation When Siblings Don't Help with Aging Parents*. DailyCaring. Retrieved September 23, 2022, from https://dailycaring.com/6-ways-to-improve-the-situation-when-siblings-dont-help-with-aging-parents/

Bursack, C. B. (2021, March 31). *Caregiving With Siblings: Resolving Issues While Caring for Parents*. © 2007-2022 AgingCare All Rights Reserved. Retrieved September 23, 2022, from https://www.agingcare.com/articles/sibling-rela tionships-resolving-issues-while-caring-for-parents-203842.htm

Can I get paid to care for a family member? (2021, February 13). Family Caregiver Alliance. Retrieved September 23, 2022, from https://www.caregiver.org/ faq/can-i-get-paid-to-care-for-a-family-member/

Can I get paid to care for a family member? (2021b, February 13). Family Caregiver Alliance. Retrieved September 23, 2022, from https://www.care giver.org/faq/can-i-get-paid-to-care-for-a-family-member/

Halpern, J. (2020, December 29). *MyElder | If You Pay Relatives To Provide Care, You Might Want To Have A Contract*. Myelder. Retrieved September 23,

2022, from https://myelder.com/if-you-pay-relatives-to-provide-care-you-might-want-to-have-a-contract/

Hiring In-Home Help. (2022, April 21). Family Caregiver Alliance. Retrieved September 23, 2022, from https://www.caregiver.org/resource/hiring-home-help/

Samuels, C. (2021, May 10). *Home Care vs. Home Health Care: What's the Difference?* Retrieved September 23, 2022, from https://www.aplacefor mom.com/caregiver-resources/articles/home-care-vs-home-health-care

Care, I. H. (2020, February 28). *The Unseen Liabilities of Hiring a Caregiver Directly | Personally Hiring a Caregiver.* InHomeCare. Retrieved September 23, 2022, from https://www.inhomecare.com/the-unseen-liabilities-of-hiring-a-caregiver-directly-personally-hiring-a-caregiver/

USAging. (n.d.). Retrieved September 23, 2022, from https://www.usaging.org/eldercareloc

How to Maintain a Positive Relationship With Your Hired Caregiver. (n.d.). A Place for Mom. Retrieved September 23, 2022, from https://www.aplaceformom.com/caregiver-resources/articles/keep-positive-relationship-with-care giver

Chaleff Rehwald Peterson | Caregiver Overtime. (n.d.). Retrieved September 23, 2022, from https://caregiverovertime.com/pa/overtime/

Assisted Living Placement Agencies (Pros & Cons In 2022). (2022, March 5). Sunflower Communities. Retrieved September 23, 2022, from https://sunflowercommunities.org/news/assisted-living-placement-agencies/

How To Create a Daily Routine to Benefit Seniors | Family Caregiver Tips | Amy's Helping Hands | In - Home Senior Care in Windsor & Essex County. (n.d.). 2022 Amy's Helping Hands | In - Home Senior Care in Windsor & Essex County. Retrieved September 23, 2022, from https://www.amyshelping hands.ca/family-caregiver-tips-134/how-to-create-a-daily-routine-to-bene fit-seniors

Durkin, A. (2022, April 11). *Healthy Routines Your Aging Parent Should Follow*. Anodyne. Retrieved September 23, 2022, from https://www.anodyne-services.com/2022/04/27/healthy-routines-for-aging-parents/

5 Tips For Helping Your Loved Ones Improve Their Physical Health. (n.d.). Retrieved September 23, 2022, from https://www.sunriseseniorliving.com/blog/june-2016/5-tips-for-helping-your-loved-ones-improve-their-physical-health.aspx

SALMON Health. (2022, February 3). *Senior Mental Health: 6 Ways to Improve Cognition & Emotion as We Age*. SALMON Health and Retirement. Retrieved September 23, 2022, from https://salmonhealth.com/blog/senior-mental-health/

5 Useful Ways to Maintain a Positive Attitude Toward Aging. (2019, February 8). Saunders House. Retrieved September 23, 2022, from https://www.saunder shouse.org/article/2/8/2019/5-useful-ways-maintain-positive-attitude-toward-aging

Mitchell, C. (n.d.). *Seniors and Mental Health*. Pan American Health Organization / World Health Organization. Retrieved September 23, 2022, from https://www3.paho.org/hq/index.php?option=com_content&view=article&id=9877:seniors-mental-health&Itemid=40721&lang=en#gsc.tab=0

O'Neill, F. (2022, March 28). *7 Ways to Keep Your Aging Parents Active and Engaged*. Retrieved September 23, 2022, from https://www.arborcompany.com/blog/7-ways-to-keep-your-aging-parents-active-and-engaged

Benefits of a Social Connection among Seniors. (2020, January 9). Closing the Gap. Retrieved September 23, 2022, from https://www.closingthegap.ca/bene fits-of-a-social-connection-among-seniors/

sos@prolificdigital.com. (2021, July 7). *Why Social Connection is Especially Important For Older People*. Elegance Living. Retrieved September 23, 2022, from https://elegance-living.com/why-social-connection-is-especially-important-for-older-people/

Reck, L. (2021, May 28). *10 Reasons Physical Touch is Important for Seniors (and everyone else)*. Seniors Helping Seniors® Greater Richmond In-Home Care

Services. Retrieved September 23, 2022, from https://seniorcaregreaterrich mond.com/health/physical-touch/

Sondra Jones - Chief Marketing Officer. (2022, June 13). *Importance of Touch for Seniors*. The Arbors. Retrieved September 23, 2022, from https://arborsas sistedliving.com/importance-of-touch-for-seniors/

Tips for Improving Communication with Older Patients. (n.d.). National Institute on Aging. Retrieved September 23, 2022, from https://www.nia.nih.gov/ health/tips-improving-communication-older-patients

Ortiz, M. C. R. L. (n.d.). *How to communicate with your aging parents about their health (and get them to listen).* Retrieved September 23, 2022, from https:// www.seniorlink.com/blog/how-to-communicate

Kernisan, M. L. M. D. (2022, August 31). *6 Steps to Take When Aging Parents Need Help – Even if They're Resisting.* Better Health While Aging. Retrieved September 23, 2022, from https://betterhealthwhileaging.net/6-steps-how-to-help-aging-parents-get-care/

5 Duties of a Dementia Caregiver. (2021, October 6). Hinsdale, Illinois. Retrieved September 23, 2022, from https://assistinghands.com/20/illinois/hinsdale/ blog/dementia-caregiver-duties/

Caregiver's Guide to Understanding Dementia Behaviors. (2021, July 15). Family Caregiver Alliance. Retrieved September 23, 2022, from https://www.care giver.org/resource/caregivers-guide-understanding-dementia-behaviors/

The 10 warning signs of dementia. (n.d.). Alzheimer Society of Canada. Retrieved September 23, 2022, from https://alzheimer.ca/en/about-demen tia/do-i-have-dementia/10-warning-signs-dementia

Dementia - Diagnosis and treatment - Mayo Clinic. (2021, June 17). Retrieved September 23, 2022, from https://www.mayoclinic.org/diseases-conditions/ dementia/diagnosis-treatment/drc-20352019

Sollitto, M. (2021, August 9). *Equipment and Products for Aging in Place.* © 2007-2022 AgingCare All Rights Reserved. Retrieved September 23, 2022, from https://www.agingcare.com/articles/equipment-helps-elderly-live-at-home-safely-95653.htm

Elderly Care Products Checklist for Caregivers. (2022, January 13). Burt's Rx. Retrieved September 23, 2022, from https://burtsrx.com/elderly-care-prod ucts-checklist/

The Importance of Sleep for Family Caregivers. (2019, November 14). FirstLight Home Care. Retrieved September 23, 2022, from https://www.first lighthomecare.com/blog/2018/03/15/sleep-for-family-caregivers/#:%7E: text=Lack%20of%20sleep%20can%20lead,take%20care%20of%20some-one%20else.

Cemental, R. (2022, August 19). *3 Easy Exercises to Relieve Caregiver Stress | Caring Senior Service.* Retrieved September 23, 2022, from https://www. caringseniorservice.com/blog/3-easy-exercises-to-relieve-stress

Ferguson, C. (2016, October 4). *8 Self Care Tips for Mindset Maintenance –.* Caroline Ferguson, Mindset Trainer. Retrieved September 23, 2022, from https://carolineferguson.com/self-care-for-your-mindset/

How to Practice Loving Kindness Meditation. (2020, February 11). Verywell Mind. Retrieved September 23, 2022, from https://www.verywellmind.com/how-to-practice-loving-kindness-meditation-3144786

Rosenblatt, C. (2011, February 7). *How to Say "No" to Your Mother.* Forbes. Retrieved September 23, 2022, from https://www.forbes.com/sites/carolyn rosenblatt/2011/02/07/how-to-say-no-to-your-mother/?sh=1e48427b49f3

Gotter, A. (2019, April 22). *8 Breathing Exercises to Try When You Feel Anxious.* Healthline. Retrieved September 23, 2022, from https://www.healthline. com/health/breathing-exercises-for-anxiety#alternate-nostrils

11 Common Symptoms of Depression - Mental Health. (2022, May 26). All Points North. Retrieved September 23, 2022, from https://apn.com/resources/11-common-symptoms-of-depression/

Grief and Loss. (2022, July 15). Family Caregiver Alliance. Retrieved September 23, 2022, from https://www.caregiver.org/resource/grief-and-loss/

When Caregiving Ends. (2021, May 14). Family Caregiver Alliance. Retrieved September 23, 2022, from https://www.caregiver.org/resource/when-care giving-ends/

Crossroads Hospice Charitable Foundation. (2016, September 5). *Rebuilding Your Life After Caregiving.* Retrieved September 23, 2022, from https://crhcf. org/insights/rebuilding-your-life-after-caregiving/

Crossroads Hospice Charitable Foundation. (2016, September 5). *Rebuilding Your Life After Caregiving.* Retrieved September 23, 2022, from https://crhcf. org/insights/rebuilding-your-life-after-caregiving/

Tip Sheet: Avoiding Caregiver Burnout | HealthInAging.org. (n.d.). Retrieved September 23, 2022, from https://www.healthinaging.org/tools-and-tips/ tip-sheet-avoiding-caregiver-burnout

Caregiver Burnout; Causes, Symptoms & Prevention. (n.d.). Cleveland Clinic. Retrieved September 23, 2022, from https://my.clevelandclinic.org/health/ diseases/9225-caregiver-burnout

Signs of Caregiver Burnout and How to Prevent It. (n.d.). VITAS Healthcare. Retrieved September 23, 2022, from https://www.vitas.com/family-and-caregiver-support/caregiving/caregiver-life-balance/signs-of-caregiver-burnout-and-how-to-prevent-it

Parenting While Caring for An Aging Parent. (n.d.). Mental Health America. Retrieved September 23, 2022, from https://www.mhanational.org/parent ing-while-caring-aging-parent

Fisher, M. (2020, June 25). *Causes and Symptoms of Caregiver Burnout | Called to Care | Johns Hopkins Bayview Medical Center in Baltimore, MD.* Retrieved September 23, 2022, from https://www.hopkinsmedicine.org/about/ community_health/johns-hopkins-bayview/services/called_to_care/ causes_symptoms_caregiver_burnout.html

What Is Caregiver Burnout? (2001, September 4). WebMD. Retrieved September 23, 2022, from https://www.webmd.com/healthy-aging/guide/ caregiver-recognizing-burnout

Caregiver Burnout: Steps for Coping With Stress. (n.d.). AARP. Retrieved September 23, 2022, from https://www.aarp.org/caregiving/life-balance/info-2019/caregiver-stress-burnout.html

18 Highly Effective Stress Relievers. (2022, August 8). Verywell Mind. Retrieved September 23, 2022, from https://www.verywellmind.com/tips-to-reduce-stress-3145195

Bursack, C. B. (2021a, March 29). *Caregiver Guilt: How to Stop Feeling Guilty About Elderly Parents.* © 2007-2022 AgingCare All Rights Reserved. Retrieved September 23, 2022, from https://www.agingcare.com/articles/caregiving-guilt-stop-feeling-guilty-126209.htm

Caregiver Guilt: 15 Reasons for It and 1 Way to Overcome It. (2020, February 23). Working Daughter. Retrieved September 23, 2022, from https://working daughter.com/15-reasons-caregivers-feel-guilt-1-way-overcome/

11 Ways to Cope with Feeling Unappreciated as a Caregiver. (2022, February 8). DailyCaring. Retrieved September 23, 2022, from https://dailycaring.com/11-ways-to-cope-with-feeling-unappreciated-as-a-caregiver/

Positive Affirmations For The Caregivers Home Help for Seniors, Senior Home Care Helping Seniors Live Well at Home | Home Care Powered by AUAF. (n.d.). Retrieved September 23, 2022, from https://www.homecare-aid.com/posi tive-affirmations-for-the-caregivers/

A Caregiver's Bill of Rights. (2021, October 15). Family Caregiver Alliance. Retrieved September 23, 2022, from https://www.caregiver.org/resource/caregivers-bill-rights/

Made in United States
North Haven, CT
12 November 2022

26628241R00147